BBC
RADIO 4

TODAY
PROGRAMME

PUZZLE
BOOK

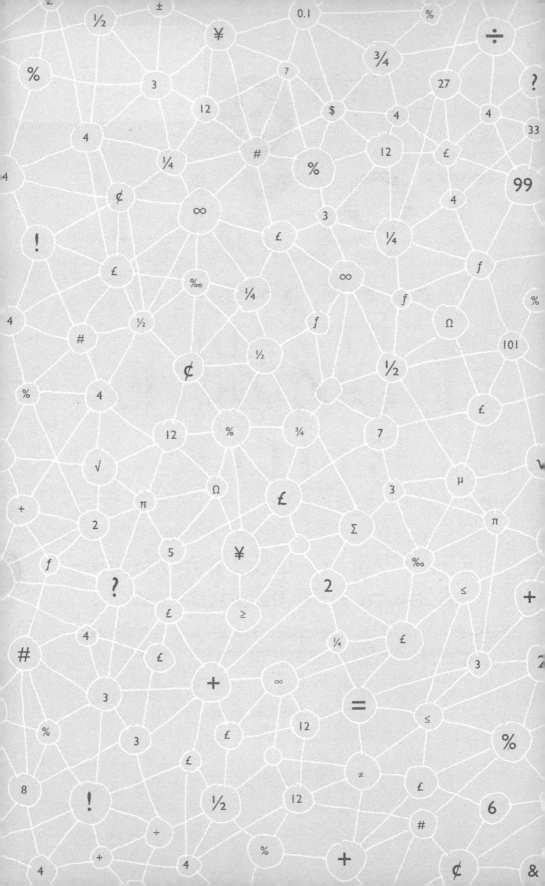

BBC RADIO 4

T⬤DAY

PROGRAMME

PUZZLE

BOOK

Over 280 cryptic, linguistic & numerical brainteasers

Puzzles from Mensa, UK Mathematics Trust, University of Cambridge, University of Oxford, Japanese puzzle masters & many more

With a foreword by Sarah Sands and introductions by Tom Feilden

CASSELL ILLUSTRATED

CONTENTS

FOREWORD

The *Today* puzzle arose naturally out of its audience. As the Queen once put it: 'At heart, we have always been a nation of problem solvers.' The *Today* audience includes many professors and, it turns out, some brilliant mathematicians. The puzzles are fiendishly hard and are often greeted by gales of laughter from the presenters. John Humphrys valiantly and wildly guesses the number 11 as an answer and twice he has turned out to be right. Meanwhile, maths teachers across the country are quietly working out the answers. Lucy Kellaway, the *FT* columnist who left to become a maths teacher, says the *Today* puzzle is the first thing she presents to her class. Scientists, tech leaders and business people are delighted about their daily victory over the arts graduates at the BBC.

We have pitched the puzzle at top French and British mathematicians, and at British and Chinese maths teachers, as a national contest. We have brought in children to solve it. One of the country's top GCSE students cracked it within minutes. The puzzles are hard but often playful, making them even more tantalising. A favourite one was this (see puzzle 235, page 129): Sarah Montague and John Humphrys go for pizza. When the pizzas arrive, the circumference of Sarah's pizza is 61cm while that of John's is only 60cm. John orders a second, customised mini-pizza to make up exactly the difference in pizza size. What is its circumference, in centimetres?

The *Today* puzzle has become a national endeavour and a BBC institution. It has appeared on Radio 4's *Dead Ringers* programme and been used light-heartedly by politicians to frame conundrums. If you can do the puzzle, you are among the smartest, and we on the *Today* team salute you.

Sarah Sands, editor of the *Today* programme

INTRODUCTION

'The first thing you have to understand is that a puzzle is not a quiz.' This was Marcus du Sautoy's first thought when I asked his advice about the idea of a daily puzzle slot on *Today* in June last year. 'You're not testing people's knowledge. It isn't about whether they can name the 21st President or remember the date of the Battle of Austerlitz. They've got Google (other search engines are available) for that. A puzzle should be something someone can work out for themselves from the clues in the question.'

And Marcus du Sautoy should know. As well as holding down a day job as the Simonyi Professor for the Public Understanding of Science at Oxford University, he's also a prolific writer, broadcaster and inveterate puzzler. If, like me, you have had to come to terms with the look of confusion and disappointment on your daughter's face as you struggle to crack the codes at the heart of Lauren Child's novels about the adventures of teen spy genius Ruby Redfort, well, you have Marcus to blame for that.

The second idea we had about the *Today* puzzles was that they shouldn't exclude all those with only the vaguest recollection of the maths they learned at school. This is the rule we have broken most often and you won't get far in chapter 4 without some basic algebra, a little geometry and Pythagoras' theorem. At some level all puzzles are mathematical, in the sense that they require you to work something out, but we've tried to limit that to the basics: arithmetic, multiplication and division, plus a bit of logical thought and a flair for problem solving – the kind of skills a young naval cadet might need to get a field gun over a moat at the Edinburgh Tattoo using only a cartwheel, three wooden poles and a piece of string.

We also thought it was important that you should be able to take the puzzle with you, pondering it on the train or while out walking the dog, without having to constantly refer back to a complicated set of numbers or table of inputs. Not everyone has a pen to hand or access to the Internet at ten to seven in the morning – and certainly not in the shower. The format has also been constrained by the need to get the presenter to read the puzzle out on air. Most, but by no means all, the *Today* puzzles fit this model. I can only apologise to Sarah Montague for forcing her to read out Bobby Seagull's Jane-Austen-inspired 'next number' puzzle in chapter 7.

The best puzzles should be, as the mathematician Alex Bellos maintains, poetry. As he says in *Can You Solve My Problems*, 'with elegance and brevity, they pique our interest, kindle our competitive spirit, test our ingenuity, and in some cases reveal universal truths'. I would only add that the best should conclude with a deeply satisfying eureka! moment. There can be only one answer, and you should know instinctively that you've got it right the moment the penny drops.

While we're here, I would like to thank Lauren Harvey for her tireless efforts sourcing, collating and checking these puzzles, and Claudia Headon for turning them into something that can be both read out on air and uploaded to our website. I also want to thank all those who have contributed puzzles for the programme and kindly allowed us to reproduce them here. Without you none of this would have been possible.

Finally, the *Today* programme's #PuzzleForToday is a bit of a work in progress. It has evolved over this first year, and will continue to do so. Look out for the introduction of more diagrams, graphs and tables as we upgrade our online capabilities. There's even some talk of going global, with special features on puzzles from different countries and cultures. Quite what the World Service will have to say about that remains to be seen.

Oh, and if you're still struggling with the 21st President of the United States and the date of the Battle of Austerlitz, the answers are: Chester A. Arthur and 2 December 1805...Napoleon won.

Tom Feilden, Science & Environment Editor on the *Today* programme

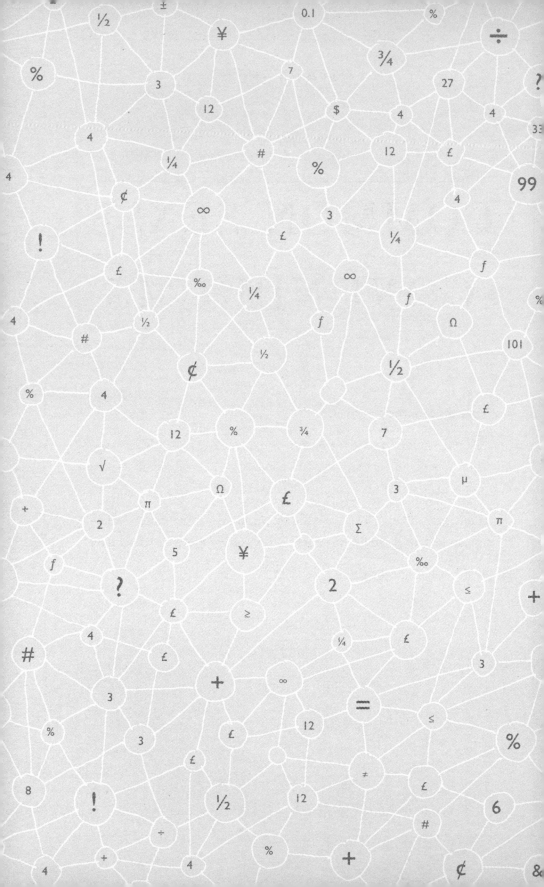

CHAPTER I

COMMON-SENSE
CONUNDRUMS

Time to get down to business.

The majority of the *Today* programme puzzles fall into this category. There's a bit of maths but for the most part it's about deductive reasoning, logical thought and problem solving.

Some tease, others – like **Starving by Numbers** or **Exclusion Zone** – are old-fashioned riddles; most tell a story you can immerse yourself in.

Grab a pencil and dive in.

1 STARVING BY NUMBERS

Late one night, famished, I bought a baker's dozen of buns but when I stopped to eat, five had fallen out of my bag. I stared at the mysterious hole in the bag, no explanation came, only a classic riddle:

'I'm more powerful than God; more evil than the devil. The poor have me; the rich need me. If you eat me, you will die.'

I looked up at the night sky for an answer. Distracted, I counted what I hoped were our planets. Slumping beneath a tree, I gorged on a form of hognut, a family pack just for me...and yet four numbers leap from my tale, to explain why I'm still hungry, tired and pale.

Paul Carden, Senior Lecturer in the Computer Science and Informatics Department,
London South Bank University

2 My name is Amy Belou. I have changed my name by deed poll to protect my father. When I was an infant, my father was obsessed about my reciting the alphabet. I wanted to learn numbers, times-tables, but my dad wouldn't let me practise. I resolved never to say a number out loud unless the letters of the words were in alphabetical order.

Many people have asked me my age over the years, but New Year's Eve 2017 was the first day I could answer.

When was I born?

Paul Carden, Senior Lecturer in the Computer Science and Informatics Department,
London South Bank University

3   **EXCLUSION ZONE**

Solve these clues:

• American rapper sounds like a sweet

• anti-Brexit voter

• a resident of Bucharest, for example

...and then cancel out all the common letters, for example, if **h** appears in each answer, remove all **h**'s.

Why does the solution exclude this puzzle's author and this puzzle's audience?

Paul Carden, Senior Lecturer in the Computer Science and Informatics Department,
London South Bank University

4   What comes next?

two-faced god,
war god,
spring goddess,
?

Hywel Carver, author of *Sodding Sums: The 10% of Maths You Actually Need*

15

5   My friend claims he's drunk 1,000 shots of rum in his life, 505 shots of vodka and 1 shot of gin.

How many shots of Metaxa has he drunk?

Hywel Carver, author of Sodding Sums: The 10% of Maths You Actually Need

6   Roger from Alpha station showed this puzzle to his friend Wilco, and after two days of head-scratching, Wilco finally solved it. He decided to tell the puzzle to his friends at Beta station, and radioed it over to them. They got the answer immediately. Can you?

Some letters of the alphabet are grouped below. Which group does Q belong in?

(AD)
(CJMORV)
(FT)
(IL)

Hywel Carver, author of Sodding Sums: The 10% of Maths You Actually Need

7   What comes next in this sequence, and why:

Y,
Y,
H,
L,
Y,
E,
Y,
T,
R,
R,
R,
?

Hywel Carver, author of *Sodding Sums: The 10% of Maths You Actually Need*

8   **THE BATHROOM MIRROR**

When Eric stands up straight in front of his vertical bathroom mirror and looks at his reflection, he is able to see down to his navel. If he steps back a few feet, is he able to see:

a) more of himself

b) the same amount

or c) less of himself?

Rob Eastaway, Director of the Maths Inspiration lecture shows

9   The population in the UK is split roughly 50–50 boys and girls. But on average who has more sisters, boys or girls?

Rob Eastaway, Director of the Maths Inspiration lecture shows

10   THE ANIMAL ENCYCLOPEDIA

I have an encyclopedia of animals on my bookshelf, which comes in two volumes. On the left is the Aardvark to Lynx volume, and next to it, on the right, is the volume for Mackerel to Zebra.

Each volume is 5cm thick. The covers are 2mm thick. I have bookmarked two pages, Aardvark and Zebra.

How far apart would you say the two bookmarks are, to the nearest centimetre?

Rob Eastaway, Director of the Maths Inspiration lecture shows

11   WHAT WAS BEHIND THE DOOR?

Yesterday I was in an office building. I walked into a room and in that room I saw a door, and on that door, some small capital letters were visible. They were CANT, then a gap, then EN. I could not see any other letters anywhere on the door. I was nowhere near the canteen. What was behind the door?

Rob Eastaway, Director of the Maths Inspiration lecture shows

12 AMERICAN QUIZ

What is surprising about the answers to these three cryptic crossword clues?

1. Gift contains name of US leader

2. Quiet inhabitant lives in the White House

3. Trump tried pens – got confused

Rob Eastaway, Director of the Maths Inspiration lecture shows

13 A fruit bowl contains **one** apple, **two** oranges and **three** bananas.

Teenage siblings Alice and Bob take it in turns removing fruit from the bowl; on their turn, they may remove one piece of fruit or two pieces of fruit of the same type. Whoever takes the last piece of fruit wins, and the other sibling must do the chores that evening.

If Alice goes first, what should she take on her first turn to force Bob to do the chores?

Daniel Griller, mathematics teacher, Olympiad problem composer
and author of the puzzle book *Elastic Numbers*

14   In every square of a ten-by-ten grid of squares there sits a frog. Then, all at once, each frog jumps randomly to a neighbouring square (diagonal jumps are forbidden). This happens several more times. Multiple frogs are allowed in the same square, but they cannot jump off the grid.

After every frog has completed 100 jumps, what is the greatest possible number of empty squares?

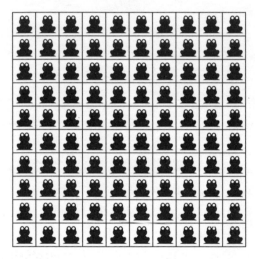

Daniel Griller, mathematics teacher, Olympiad problem composer
and author of the puzzle book *Elastic Numbers*

15   Bertrand the Barn Owl bought three books for a total of £10.80. When he looked at his receipt, he noticed that one of the books cost three times another, and one of the books cost eight times another.

How much was the cheapest book?

Daniel Griller, mathematics teacher, Olympiad problem composer
and author of the puzzle book *Elastic Numbers*

16   As punishment for cheating on yet another maths test, Dishonest Dave is forced to write out a list of 2,017 numbers.

The first two numbers are 20 and 17, and every number after these is the difference between the two previous numbers, so the first five numbers Dave must write are:

20,

17,

3,

14,

11.

What is the last number Dishonest Dave will write before his punishment is complete?

Daniel Griller, mathematics teacher, Olympiad problem composer
and author of the puzzle book *Elastic Numbers*

17   George is about to begin a strange new diet. He will eat 60 blueberries over the course of several days. Each day after the first day he will eat one more blueberry than on the previous day.

If he makes the blueberries last for as many days as possible, how many will he eat on the final day of his diet?

Daniel Griller, mathematics teacher, Olympiad problem composer
and author of the puzzle book *Elastic Numbers*

18 Alice and Bob are splitting a cake using the cut-cut-choose-choose method.

Alice cuts the cake into two pieces; then Bob cuts one of these pieces, so that there are three pieces in total.

Next, Alice chooses one piece to keep for herself, then Bob chooses a piece, and Alice takes the final piece.

Given that they each want as much cake as possible, what fraction of the original cake can Alice guarantee to take for herself?

Daniel Griller, mathematics teacher, Olympiad problem composer
and author of the puzzle book *Elastic Numbers*

19 In the Footprints Cafe, each table has three legs, each chair has four legs and all the customers and the three members of staff have 2 legs each.

There are four chairs at each table. At a certain time, three-quarters of the chairs are occupied by customers and there are 206 legs altogether in the cafe.

How many chairs does the cafe have?

University of Cambridge's NRICH project (nrich.maths.org), in collaboration with the UK Mathematics Trust

20 Two adults and two children wish to cross a river. They make a raft but it will carry only the weight of one adult or two children. What is the minimum number of times the raft must cross the river to get all four people to the other side?

NOTE: The raft may not cross the river without at least one person on board.

NRICH project (nrich.maths.org), University of Cambridge in collaboration with the UK Mathematics Trust

21 The Queen of Hearts has lost her tarts! She is sure that those knaves who have not eaten the tarts will tell her the truth and the guilty knaves will tell lies. When questioned, the five knaves declare:

Knave 1: 'One of us ate them'

Knave 2: 'Two of us ate them'

Knave 3: 'Three of us ate them'

Knave 4: 'Four of us ate them'

Knave 5: 'Five of us ate them'

How many of the knaves were honest?

NRICH project (nrich.maths.org), University of Cambridge in collaboration with the UK Mathematics Trust

22   Albert Einstein is experimenting with two unusual clocks that both have 24-hour digital displays.

One clock runs at twice the normal speed.

The other clock goes backwards, but at the normal speed.

Both clocks show the correct time at 13:00.

At what time do the displays on the clocks next agree?

NRICH project (nrich.maths.org), University of Cambridge in collaboration with the UK Mathematics Trust

23   Becky has a 24-hour digital clock on a glass tabletop. When she looked at the clock at 13:08, she noticed that the reflection of the display in the tabletop looked exactly the same as the digital clock, whereas a minute earlier it hadn't.

How many times in a 24-hour period will the digital display and its reflection appear exactly the same?

NRICH project (nrich.maths.org), University of Cambridge in collaboration with the UK Mathematics Trust

24   One year, there were exactly four Tuesdays and exactly four Fridays in October.

On what day of the week did Halloween, 31 October, fall that year?

NRICH project (nrich.maths.org), University of Cambridge in collaboration with the UK Mathematics Trust

25   Kitty has nine vintage patchwork squares, each a different size. Their side lengths are:

1, 4, 7, 8, 9, 10, 14, 15 and 18 inches.

She joins them together, with no gaps and no overlaps, to form a rectangular quilt.

Can you find the dimensions of the finished quilt, and work out how Kitty fitted the squares together?

NRICH project (nrich.maths.org), University of Cambridge

26   Is it possible for a boat to visit every sea area in the Shipping Forecast once, and once only, on a single voyage?

Boats can't sail across 'corners', so to go from Dogger to Fisher, the boat must sail through either Forties or German Bight.

School of Mathematics at the University of Manchester

27   You are queuing to get onto a busy train. As luck would have it, there are exactly the same number of seats as passengers, 220, and all but one of the passengers have seat reservations.

Unfortunately, the seat reservation system isn't working. People will sit in their reserved seat if possible, but if their seat is occupied, rather than making a fuss, they will just pick another empty seat at random.

If you are last to board the train, what is the probability that your reserved seat will be available?

School of Mathematics at the University of Manchester

28   A bakery's new signature ring doughnut is iced with several different colours, and each coloured region must share a part of its boundary (more than just a point) with regions of every other colour.

What is the maximum number of colours that can be used?

School of Mathematics at The University of Manchester

29   **TROLL AGE PUZZLE**

A troll's age and his son's age are the same with the digits reversed. A year ago the troll was twice as old as his son.

How old are the troll and his son?

Dr Steve Humble MBE, Head of Education, Newcastle University

30 MILLIONAIRE POCKET MONEY

If you were given pocket money of 1p the first week, then 2p the second week, 4p the third week, 8p the fourth week and so on, doubling up each week, how long would it be before you have saved £1 million?

Dr Steve Humble MBE, Head of Education, Newcastle University

31 WHAT IS IN THE BOX?

The teacher placed a box on his desk. He asked one of his students to take out five balls without looking into the box.

All five balls selected were blue.

'There was a 50 per cent chance of that happening,' said the teacher.

What is the smallest number of balls that could have been placed in the box for this to happen, and how many of them would have been blue?

Dr Steve Humble MBE, Head of Education, Newcastle University

32 HOW OLD IS YOUR FRIEND?

If your friend said they were 30 years old not counting Saturdays or Sundays, how old would they really be?

Dr Steve Humble MBE, Head of Education, Newcastle University

33   You travelled 5km south, then 5km west, then 5km north and returned where you started, meeting a bear on the journey.

Are there any other points on the Earth where you could have the same experience, but without the bear?

Dr Gihan Marasingha, Senior Lecturer in Mathematics at the University of Exeter

34   At 3pm, while pondering the fate of Big Ben, the Prime Minister noted that the hands of the great clock were perpendicular.

What is the first time, after the 7pm division, at which this phenomenon will reoccur?

Dr Gihan Marasingha, Senior Lecturer in Mathematics at the University of Exeter

35 Patrick needs to take an antibiotic four times a day, at equally spaced intervals.

He takes his first pill at 6am and his last pill at 10pm.

How long should he wait between taking successive pills?

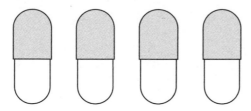

Dr Gihan Marasingha, Senior Lecturer in Mathematics at the University of Exeter

36 In how many ways can the letters of the word **EXETER** be arranged?

For example, REETEX is one such arrangement.

Dr Gihan Marasingha, Senior Lecturer in Mathematics at the University of Exeter

37 Trevor Vines Buff notices that TV programmes display copyright years in Roman numerals. So far this century, no date requires more than six letters.

If TV-making began in the year I, what would be the first date to require 12 letters?

Dr Gihan Marasingha, Senior Lecturer in Mathematics at the University of Exeter

38 A survey is taken of 50 people, each of whom listen to at least one of the *Today* programme, *The Archers* and *Woman's Hour*.

32 listen to *Today*,
26 to *The Archers*,
and 30 to *Woman's Hour*.

Also,
15 listen to both *Today* and *The Archers*,
18 to both *Today* and *Woman's Hour*,
and 16 to both *Woman's Hour* and *The Archers*.

How many listen to all three programmes?

Dr Gihan Marasingha, Senior Lecturer in Mathematics at the University of Exeter

39 Although partial women's suffrage came to the UK mainland in 1918, it had a precedent in an Act of Tynwald, the Isle of Man's legislature, giving the franchise to unmarried women and widows.

There was a positively beastly difference in years between the enactment of this legislation and that of a much earlier great charter.

In what year did Manx spinsters gain the vote?

Dr Gihan Marasingha, Senior Lecturer in Mathematics at the University of Exeter

40 What links:

a sitting Conservative MP called Richard,
an erstwhile Radio 4 stalwart called Henry
and a cab driver in Bath called Dave?

Mark Mason, author of the book *Question Time: A Journey Round Britain's Quizzes*

41 They were patented in London in 1845.
They are often used in the castration of farm animals.
At the height of his success, the Colombian drugs baron Pablo Escobar was spending $1,000 a week on them.

What are they?

Mark Mason, author of the book *Question Time: A Journey Round Britain's Quizzes*

42 A poem often recited during a professional career that lasted from the 1960s to the 1980s has the second line, 'Your hand can't hit what your eye can't see.'

But its first line is much better known.

Who wrote it?

Mark Mason, author of the book *Question Time: A Journey Round Britain's Quizzes*

43 Its official title was ***Blood Swept Lands and Seas of Red***.

How was it more popularly known?

Mark Mason, author of the book *Question Time: A Journey Round Britain's Quizzes*

44 Noel Edmonds damaged Elton John's garden, and Nick Mason of Pink Floyd damaged Jeremy Clarkson's garden, in the same way.

How?

Mark Mason, author of the book *Question Time: A Journey Round Britain's Quizzes*

45 Who, in October 2016, told the US talk show host Stephen Colbert that he was looking forward to working in an office that had corners?

Mark Mason, author of the book *Question Time: A Journey Round Britain's Quizzes*

46 Which is the only letter of the alphabet not to appear in the name of any US state?

Mark Mason, author of the book *Question Time: A Journey Round Britain's Quizzes*

47 The only time it has happened in British history was from 2010 to 2016, when the value was 600.

What are we talking about?

Mark Mason, author of the book *Question Time: A Journey Round Britain's Quizzes*

48 The shortest is in the Northwest, and is four.

The longest is in the West Midlands, and is how many?

Mark Mason, author of the book *Question Time: A Journey Round Britain's Quizzes*

49 A change in the wildlife on Mauritius in the late 17th century gave rise to which modern expression?

Mark Mason, author of the book *Question Time: A Journey Round Britain's Quizzes*

50   Number 1 was *Phil Collins*.

Number 2 was QUEEN.

Number 11 (just to keep John Humphrys happy) was the **Pet Shop Boys**.

Number 96 was `Ed Sheeran`.

What are we talking about?

Mark Mason, author of the book *Question Time: A Journey Round Britain's Quizzes*

51   In which country would you find:

'Saint Mary's Church in a hollow of white hazel near the swirling whirlpool of the church of Saint Tysilio with a red cave'?

Mark Mason, author of the book *Question Time: A Journey Round Britain's Quizzes*

52   A prime number is a whole number bigger than 1 that can be divided exactly by 1 and by itself but not by any other number.

The highest prime number you can score with one dart is 19.

What's the highest prime number you can score with two darts?

Mark Mason, author of the book *Question Time: A Journey Round Britain's Quizzes*

53   'You eat more than I do,' said Tweedledee to Tweedledum.

'That is not true,' said Tweedledum to Tweedledee.

'You are both wrong,' said Alice, to them both.

'You are right,' said the White Rabbit to Alice.

How many of the four statements are true?

'Perplex', a brain-teaser app made by the UK Mathematics Trust and The Open University

54   We have all heard the saying:

'Red sky at night, shepherd's delight...red sky in the morning, shepherd's warning.'

Let's say that our shepherd makes his weather predictions based on the morning sky, predicting a storm when the sky is red and no storm when there are clear skies.

Assume that there is a storm, on average, every second day, and a red sky in the morning can be expected every fourth day and always means a storm.

How often will the shepherd be correct?

Dr Jennifer Rogers, The Royal Statistical Society and Department of Statistics, University of Oxford

55   What connects the following seven words?

tape
squash
pages
beans
blood
snake
wood

School of Mathematics and Statistics at the University of Sheffield

56 TWO SLIGHTLY FISHY SCORING SYSTEMS

Each day a keen angler rates their catch using a scoring system.

On Monday, they catch a salmon worth eight points.
On Tuesday, they rate a cod at six points,
On Wednesday a pollack scores 15 points.

How much is the bass on Thursday worth?

School of Mathematics and Statistics at the University of Sheffield

57 A CURSED PROBLEM

A piece of string is attached to the corner of a cube. The cube is suspended by the string and lowered into a bucket of water so that exactly half of the cube is submerged.

What shape is made by the intersection of the cube with the surface of the water?

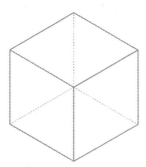

School of Mathematics and Statistics at the University of Sheffield

58   Before lunch, Peter sits with Alexandra, Isolde sits with Richard, and Edward sits with Debra.

After lunch their seating arrangement is randomised.

What is the probability that at least one of the pairs sits together for the full day?

School of Mathematics and Statistics at the University of Sheffield

59   A maths lecturer gets two hate-letters for every third Radio 4 puzzle he produces, and one in five of these is followed up by an apology from the letter-writer.

If half the apologies are insincere (and hence null), how many unapologetically hate-filled letters will he have received by his 76th puzzle?

Dr Roger Teichmann, Lecturer in Philosophy, St Hilda's College, University of Oxford

60 Here is a balance:

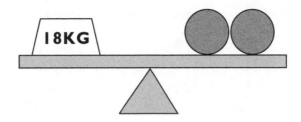

Here is another balance:

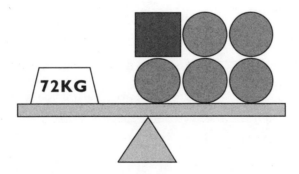

Work out the weight of two s.

Tes, which hosts a full curriculum of maths lessons developed in collaboration with White Rose Maths, available free on its resources site

61   In the pyramids the two numbers below add to the make the number above.

Complete these two pyramids:

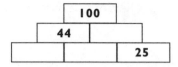

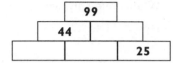

What is the value of the grey box?

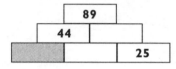

62   Here are three identical rectangles. Part of each shape has been shaded. What fraction of the middle shape is shaded?

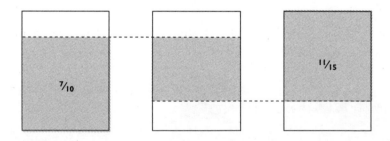

63   I lay out eight ordinary playing cards face up in a neat two-by-four rectangular grid on the table and, while I close my eyes, my friend rotates one of the cards by 180 degrees by sliding it on the table face up.

When I open my eyes, I tell my friend which one has been rotated. How did I do it?

Dr Lynda White, Principal Teaching Fellow in Experimental Design in the Department of Mathematics at Imperial College London

64   According to the Highway Code, which road can carry the most traffic in terms of cars per hour:

A minor road,

a B road

or a single carriageway A road?

Professor Chris Budd OBE, Department for Mathematical Sciences at the University of Bath

65   What is longer, the height of a standard (Nonic) pint glass or its rim's circumference?

Dr Kit Yates, Department for Mathematical Sciences at the University of Bath

66 I have a rectangular bar of chocolate consisting of four rows of three small chocolate squares each.

Being of a generous disposition, I want to divide the bar into the 12 small squares to give to my friends. I can break the bar in many different ways.

For example, I might start by breaking it into two 2 × 3 bars or perhaps three 1 × 4 bars and then subdivide the resulting pieces.

At each stage a cut is made along a single straight line between some of the small squares until all 12 squares of chocolate are separated (no stacking of one piece on top of another allowed as it makes too much of a mess!).

Is there a method for doing this that involves the least number of such cuts?

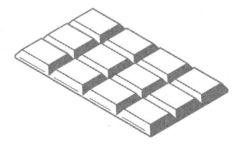

Dr Lynda White, Principal Teaching Fellow in Experimental Design in the Department of Mathematics at Imperial College London

67   I have a clock with a minute hand and an hour hand on a conventional face.

At what times will the two hands be in exactly the same position?

Professor Chris Budd OBE, Department for Mathematical Sciences at the University of Bath

68   Is it worth keeping your old calendar? How many years would you have to wait before you could use it again? That is, that the same dates fall on the same exact day of the week.

Dr Steve Humble MBE, Head of Education, Newcastle University

69   How likely is it that two or more people in London have the same number of hairs on their head?

Dr Kit Yates, Department for Mathematical Sciences at the University of Bath

70   In the race to procreate a mixed-gender rugby union team, your friend has had 13 kids. So far you've only managed 12.

What is the probability that your friend has more girls than you do?

Dr Kit Yates, Department for Mathematical Sciences at the University of Bath

71   As a surprising fact you are told that three of the first five presidents died on 4 July. They are, in order:

George Washington;
John Adams;
Thomas Jefferson;
James Madison;
and James Monroe.

Without any prior knowledge you can be relatively sure of naming one of the presidents who died on the 4 July. Which one?

Dr Kit Yates, Department for Mathematical Sciences at the University of Bath

72   Are there more pairs of twins of the same sex or of different sexes?

Dr Kit Yates, Department for Mathematical Sciences at the University of Bath

73 The Head of the Weather Department says that right now, there are two different places in the world that have exactly the same temperature and exactly the same wind speed.

Is she right?

Professor Gregory Sankaran, Department for Mathematical Sciences at the University of Bath

74 Rearrange each of the following to give the name of a football team. What are the three teams?

a) **OVER TEN**

b) **SEVENTH WARLORD MANPOWER**

c) **THE PHOTO TANTRUMS**

Mensa, the High IQ society

75 Puzzleland needs a new flag. It will be a two-by-three grid of squares, and each square will be painted red, white or blue.

Every colour must appear, but no two squares sharing an edge may have the same colour. In how many ways can the flag be designed?

Daniel Griller, mathematics teacher, Olympiad problem composer
and author of the puzzle book *Elastic Numbers*

76   Here's a teaser you will not have heard:

A Puzzle for Today — and then no more,

A literary tour around the world,

And link, that joins in one these writers four.

Our tale begins with feline revelry

As Owl and Pussy Cat set out by boat,

Then son of Rome (exiled to the Black Sea)

Whose 'Metamorphoses' are still of note.

Sedition? Scandal? Even blasphemy?

The optimism of Candide ne'er stops!

And last, but certainly by no means least,

Is The Love Song of J Alfred Prufrock.

So seek us the way these writers intertwine;

It's all you need to be my Valentine.

Bobby Seagull, Cambridge University Doctorate student, school maths teacher
and author of The Life Changing Magic of Numbers

77 DAM BUSTER PUZZLE

In May 1943, 19 Lancaster Bombers took off from RAF Scampton on the Dam Busters mission.

Bouncing bombs were used to destroy German dams. The planes famously flew fast and low, at 240mph and a height of only 60ft. This was to achieve a perfect bounce angle at the water surface.

Bomber Harris said that 60ft was too dangerous, preferring twice the height at 120ft.

At this height, how much faster would the planes have had to fly to achieve the same perfect bounce angle?

Hugh Hunt, Reader in Engineering Dynamics and Vibration at Trinity College, Cambridge

78

Mishal Husain is doing a magic trick for Justin Webb. She distributes 100 balls in four boxes of different colours, so that no box is empty. Each ball is marked with a number from 1 to 100 (with a different number on each ball). Then, while blindfolded, she asks Justin to pick a random ball from three of the boxes (one ball per box), add together the numbers on the selected balls and yell the sum out loud. Then Mishal proceeds to tell the audience which box was NOT selected by Justin, while she is still blindfolded.

How did she do it? Can you think of a way for her to separate the balls before the show, so that she aways understands which box is not used?

Dr Nicos Georgiou, Senior Lecturer of Mathematics at the University of Sussex

79   Sophie paints a different positive number on each face of a cube,
so that the sum of the numbers on each pair of adjacent faces is
a multiple of six.

What is the smallest possible sum of all six numbers?

Daniel Griller, mathematics teacher, Olympiad problem composer
and author of the puzzle book *Elastic Numbers*

80   Ahead of Mother's Day on Sunday, one of her three children said the
following to their mum.

'Sorry, mummy, I haven't got you a Mother's Day gift yet, but I've got
a mathematical treat for you. I've noticed that if you square the age
of all of your three children and then sum them up, it adds up to your
age, which is also a square number.'

So the question is, assuming the mother has not reached retirement
age, what is the age of the mother and her three children?

Bobby Seagull, Cambridge University Doctorate student, school maths teacher
and author of *The Life Changing Magic of Numbers*

48

81 For St Patrick's Day, we visit a pub where the owner is a fan of the action film series *Die Hard*.

Inspired by the films, the owner challenges you to give him a pint of beer with a strange restriction. You only have an empty five-pint jar and an empty three-pint jar to measure with.

You have ten pints of beer to achieve this task and many willing friends that can drink the beer for you.

So what is your strategy to create one pint of beer?

Bobby Seagull, Cambridge University Doctorate student, school maths teacher
and author of *The Life Changing Magic of Numbers*

82 *UNIVERSITY CHALLENGE*

After the final, all eight contestants shake hands with every single finalist from their team and the opposition team.

Every single contestant also shakes hands with quiz master Jeremy Paxman.

So your starter for ten puzzle is: 'How many different handshakes are there in total?'

Bobby Seagull, Cambridge University Doctorate student, school maths teacher
and author of *The Life Changing Magic of Numbers*

83   COMMONWEALTH GAMES PUZZLE

What links the following?

A killer whale in 1994,

An orangutan in 1998,

A cat in 2002,

A cockatoo in 2006,

A tiger in 2010,

A thistle in 2014 and

A koala in 2018.

Bobby Seagull, Cambridge University Doctorate student, school maths teacher
and author of *The Life Changing Magic of Numbers*

84   In the standard DD/MM/YYYY date format (with two digits for the day, two for the month and four for the year), what is the next date on which every digit will be different?

Daniel Griller, mathematics teacher, Olympiad problem composer
and author of the puzzle book *Elastic Numbers*

85 To celebrate the first anniversary of his French Presidency, Emmanuel Macron receives gifts from many world leaders at the Élysée Palace.

From nearby countries:

Theresa May sends a lantern,

Angela Merkel sends a bottle

and Vladimir Putin sends a mirror.

From further afield:

Narendra Modi sends a necktie,

King Jong-un sends a piano

and Donald Trump sends a watch.

Following these gifts, what might make a logical suggestion for the Canadian Prime Minister, Justin Trudeau, to send to President Macron?

Bobby Seagull, Cambridge University Doctorate student, school maths teacher
and author of *The Life Changing Magic of Numbers*

86   LONDON MARATHON PUZZLE

An elite athlete revealed a curious training plan with his running partner. Over several days, he ran the following route:

Liverpool → Wigan → Manchester → Crewe → Shrewsbury → Stafford.

His training partner did the following route:

Peterborough → Northampton → Oxford → Reading → central London → Luton → Oxford again.

Assuming neither runner was constricted by roads and was free to run the shortest distance between these locations, explain why they took these particular routes.

Bobby Seagull, Cambridge University Doctorate student, school maths teacher and author of *The Life Changing Magic of Numbers*

87   EUROVISION SONG CONTEST

Entries from France, Germany, Spain, Italy and the United Kingdom are guaranteed places in the final every year.

With the following theoretical song choices, why might only the UK entry get the infamous 'nul points'?

France's song is 'Can humans only imagine roads?'

Germany's song is 'Very original ice cream eggs'.

Spain's song is 'Super clever aliens learn eternally'.

Italy's song is 'Love you really in colour'.

The UK's song is 'Animal zoos exert regal opulence'.

So to remind you again, your puzzle is to work out why the UK entry was the only one to get zero points?

Bobby Seagull, Cambridge University Doctorate student, school maths teacher
and author of *The Life Changing Magic of Numbers*

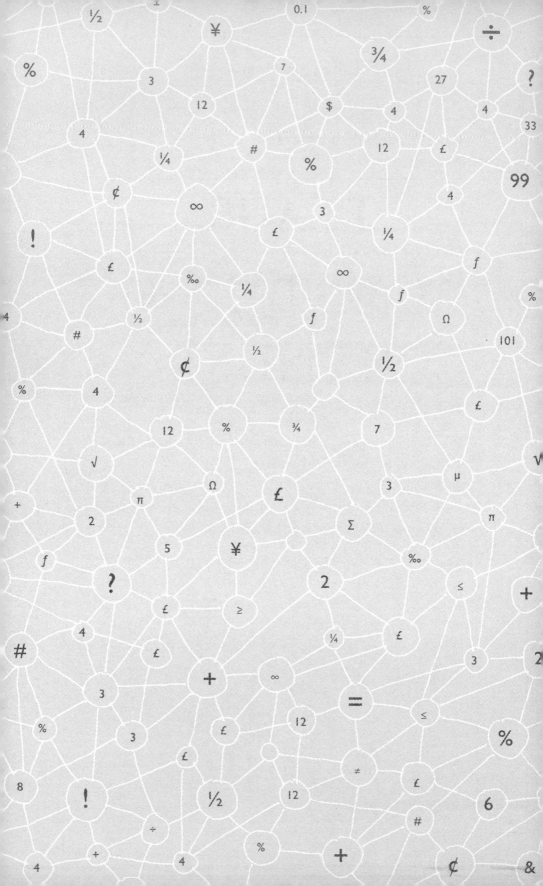

CHAPTER 2

FLAGS, CAPITALS & NATIONS

Bobby Seagull, who won acclaim as a contestant on *University Challenge* opposite Eric Monkman, seems particularly obsessed with puzzles about countries, their flags and sporting prowess.

This is a chapter for all the geographers out there.

88 Here is a sequence of countries.

1 = Paraguay

2 = Thailand

3 = Australia

4 = Republic of Ireland

Why would this sequence fail to continue at **5** but pick up again at **6** with Sierra Leone?

Bobby Seagull, Cambridge University Doctorate student, school maths teacher
and author of *The Life Changing Magic of Numbers*

89 **1** = Spain

2 = Turkey

3 = Canada

4 = Uzbekistan

What is **5**?

Bobby Seagull, Cambridge University Doctorate student, school maths teacher
and author of *The Life Changing Magic of Numbers*

90   **5** = Stockholm
     10 = Los Angeles
     15 = Helsinki
     20 = Munich
     25 = Barcelona

What is **30**?

Bobby Seagull, Cambridge University Doctorate student, school maths teacher
and author of *The Life Changing Magic of Numbers*

91   France is Marseille,
     Germany is Hamburg,
     Italy is Milan,
     Spain is Barcelona.

What is the UK?

Bobby Seagull, Cambridge University Doctorate student, school maths teacher
and author of *The Life Changing Magic of Numbers*

92   **6** = South Africa

5 = Guyana

4 = Malaysia

3 = Belgium

2 = Nigeria

Why would we have had an answer to 1 back in 2011 but no longer now?

Bobby Seagull, Cambridge University Doctorate student, school maths teacher
and author of *The Life Changing Magic of Numbers*

93   Consider a sequence of square numbers.

1 is France,

4 is Switzerland,

9 is Austria

and **16** is again France.

Why do we have to wait until 2019 to find out the next square number
of 25 in this sequence?

Bobby Seagull, Cambridge University Doctorate student, school maths teacher
and author of *The Life Changing Magic of Numbers*

94   What comes next:

Monaco, France, Sweden, Germany

Italy, Vatican, Spain, Hungary

Poland, United Kingdom, San Marino, Serbia

Irish Republic, Albania, Belgium, ____?____

Paul Carden, Senior Lecturer in the Computer Science and Informatics Department,
London South Bank University

95   If AFC Bournemouth = Albania,
      Brighton = Finland,
      Liverpool = Tonga,
      Southampton = Yemen,
      then give an answer for Arsenal = ?

Hywel Carver, author of *Sodding Sums: The 10% of Maths You Actually Need*

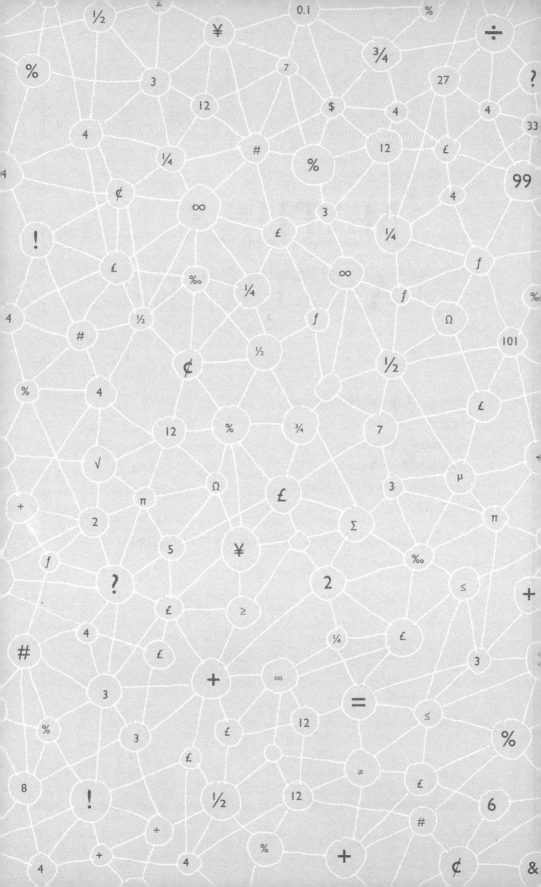

CHAPTER 3

MATHS &

LANGUAGE

DON'T PANIC.

These puzzles may look daunting but they're actually pretty simple and some deductive reasoning and logical thought will get you a long way. If you do get stuck, try breaking them down into their constituent parts and go through each puzzle step by step.

We'll start with some easy ones, so, as the quantum physicists like to say, 'Shut up and calculate!'

96 What is $5 + 3 \times 10$?

Hywel Carver, author of *Sodding Sums: The 10% of Maths You Actually Need*

97 You roll a dice twice and get a six both times.

If you roll it again, what is the probability of getting another six?

Hywel Carver, author of *Sodding Sums: The 10% of Maths You Actually Need*

98 GIANT MONSTER PUZZLE

A Giant's head is 60cm long and its legs are as long as its head and three-quarters of its body.

If its body is a third of its whole length, how big is the Giant?

Dr Steve Humble MBE, Head of Education, Newcastle University

99 MONSTER BLACK DOG PUZZLE

A dog runs a mile in three minutes with the wind and returns in four minutes against the wind.

How long would it take the dog to run the mile if there was no wind?

Dr Steve Humble MBE, Head of Education, Newcastle University

100 ONE + ONE = TWO

Each letter represents a different digit and the challenge is to discover which digit each letter represents.

There are in fact 16 different possible answers to this puzzle.

Can you find them all?

Dr Steve Humble MBE, Head of Education, Newcastle University

101

One pub is doing a three-for-the-price-of-two during happy hour, and a second pub is doing 30 per cent off.

Which is better?

Hywel Carver, author of *Sodding Sums: The 10% of Maths You Actually Need*

102 The country Utopia has a currency of 1p, 5p and 6p coins. Thomas has lots of 5p and 6p coins, but no 1p coins.

What is the largest amount of money that he can't make with the coins he has?

Hywel Carver, author of *Sodding Sums: The 10% of Maths You Actually Need*

103 What is the largest sum of money you can have in coins, and still not be able to give someone exactly £10?

UK Mathematics Trust (www.ukmt.org.uk)

104 There are three children in a family: twin girls and a boy.

The product of their ages is 175.

What is the sum of their ages?

UK Mathematics Trust (www.ukmt.org.uk)

105 In how many different ways can 2017 be written as the sum of two prime numbers?

UK Mathematics Trust (www.ukmt.org.uk)

106 What is the smallest number of colours needed to paint the faces of a regular dodecahedron so that adjacent faces have different colours?

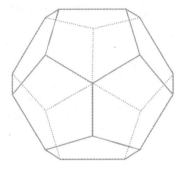

UK Mathematics Trust (www.ukmt.org.uk)

107 In this cryptarithm, each of the different letters stands for a different whole number between zero and nine.

TWO + TWO = FOUR

There is more than one possible solution.

Can you find them all?

NRICH project (nrich.maths.org), University of Cambridge

108 Dr Livingwood is contemplating a perilous journey on the Kolmogorov River. He knows that 99 per cent of all travellers die on this journey.

To allay his fears, he seeks out the local soothsayer. Her brochure contains data on previous predictions: from a set of 100 travellers who met a sticky end, she correctly predicted the demise of 90. Conversely, from a different set of 200 travellers who lived to tell the tale, she foretold a safe journey for 192.

She reads Livingwood's leaves. They betoken a calm and uneventful journey.

How should he feel about his upcoming adventure?

Dr Gihan Marasingha, Senior Lecturer in Mathematics at the University of Exeter

109 Carol starts teaching at a new school and is told how many children will be in her class. She immediately deduces that at least five children were born in the same month.

What can you say about the size of her class?

Dr Gihan Marasingha, Senior Lecturer in Mathematics at the University of Exeter

I I0 **MINNIE'S MINIATURE RESTAURANT** can seat four diners.

The room can be arranged in five ways:

as a table of four,

as a three and a one,

as two twos,

as a two and two ones,

or as four ones.

Her latest venture can seat ten diners.

How many arrangements are possible?

Dr Gihan Marasingha, Senior Lecturer in Mathematics at the University of Exeter

I I I Alien bees invade Earth.

On the third and fourth days of its life, each bee gives birth to a live clone, then dies at the end of its fourth day. The invasion begins with one bee.

How many bees are there at the end of the 20th day?

Dr Gihan Marasingha, Senior Lecturer in Mathematics at the University of Exeter

112 An MP has a book of ten jokes. Each time she gives a TV interview, she likes to read three jokes from the book.

How many interviews can she give before she has to repeat the same set of jokes twice?

Dr Gihan Marasingha, Senior Lecturer in Mathematics at the University of Exeter

113 Under budgetary pressure, Isca Cathedral decides to save money by recycling candles. One new candle can be formed from ten melted candle stubs.

In total, how many candles can the cathedral burn from an initial inventory of 2,017 candles?

Dr Gihan Marasingha, Senior Lecturer in Mathematics at the University of Exeter

114 If all four contestants in an episode of *Mastermind* shake hands with each other, how many handshakes will there be?

Mark Mason, author of the book *Question Time: A Journey Round Britain's Quizzes*

115 As visiting captain during the 1998/9 Ashes series in Australia, Alec Stewart was allowed to call the toss of the coin before each of the five matches. He lost all five.

The odds of this happening are 1 in how many?

Mark Mason, author of the book *Question Time: A Journey Round Britain's Quizzes*

116 There are 400 llamas and alpacas in total.

Three-quarters of the llamas are sold at market.
One-third of the alpacas are sold at market.
There are 125 llamas and alpacas left in total.

How many llamas were sold at the market?

Tes, which hosts a full curriculum of maths lessons developed in collaboration with White Rose Maths, available free on its resources site

117 Farmer Troy has 242 goats and cows in total. He sells half of the goats and buys 28 more cows. In the end he has three times as many cows as goats.

How many cows did he have to start with?

Tes, which hosts a full curriculum of maths lessons developed in collaboration with White Rose Maths, available free on its resources site

118 Yasmin has three jars of bugs.

There are seven more bugs in the first jar than the second.

There are three fewer bugs in the third jar than the second.

There are 40 bugs in total.

How many bugs are in the first jar?

Tes, which hosts a full curriculum of maths lessons developed in collaboration with White Rose Maths, available free on its resources site

119 I have a lot of books in my attic: at least 100, but not more than 500.

If I stack them in fives, there is one left over.

If I stack them in nines, there are two left over.

If I stack them in eights, there are three left over.

How many books are there in my attic?

Professor Gregory Sankaran, Department for Mathematical Sciences at the University of Bath

120 A coffee costs £2, and comes with a free sticker. By collecting six stickers, you can claim a free coffee, which also comes with a free sticker.

What's the minimum amount you need to spend to get 25 coffees?

NRICH project (nrich.maths.org), University of Cambridge

121 This will make your head spin.

I was born on New Year's Day together with my evil twin. I hand you a piece of paper containing only the years that my evil twin was born and died, separated by a hyphen. The document reads:

'1661–1961'.

How old was my evil twin when they died?

School of Mathematics and Statistics at the University of Sheffield

122 After a long day working on the cash register, Jill realises that she can make any amount of change from 1p to 10p from a collection of four coins: one 1p, two 2p and one 5p piece. No smaller collection suffices.

What is the smallest number of standard UK coins that can be used to make any change from 1p to £1.10?

Dr Gihan Marasingha, Senior Lecturer in Mathematics at the University of Exeter

123 A caterpillar crawls to the vegetable patch at a speed of 9 metres per hour. After overindulging, the caterpillar returns, over exactly the same distance, at 3 metres per hour.

What is the caterpillar's average speed over the entire journey?

Mensa, the High IQ society

124 What number should replace the question mark in this sequence?

6
?
11
16
27
43
70

125 Use the letters given to complete the star so that two five-letter words, one four-letter word and two words of two letters can be read. What are the words?

A B E E H N R T Y

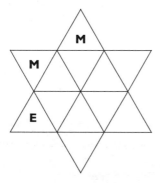

126 Rearrange the order of the following words and place one on each row of the grid. If placed correctly, the name of a country will be read down each shaded column. What are the two countries?

EXCITED
LIZARDS
IMPRESS
COMPANY
ICICLES
MEADOWS

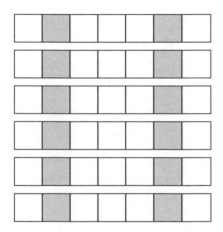

127 Find a word to fit the first clue, then add one letter to give a word to fit the second clue. What are the two words?

A MODE OF TRANSPORT   **TO BRAG**

128 A 440-yard long train, travelling at 40mph, enters a tunnel of one and a half miles in length.

How many seconds will elapse between the moment the front of the train enters the tunnel and the moment the end of the train clears the tunnel?

Mensa, the High IQ society

129 Here is an unusual safe. Each of the buttons must be pressed once only in the correct order to reach the centre X and open the safe. The number of moves and direction to move is marked on each button.

Which button is the first you must press?

1 E	4 S	2 S	4 S	4 W
1 S	1 S	2 E	1 W	3 W
4 E	1 S	X	2 N	1 W
2 N	1 E	2 W	1 E	3 N
4 E	1 W	4 N	1 N	2 W

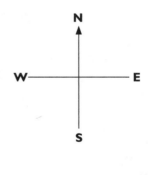

Mensa, the High IQ society

130 The alphabet is written here but some letters are missing. Arrange the missing letters to give two eight-letter words. What are they?

B D F G H J K L M P Q S U V W X Y Z

131 What number should replace the question mark in the sequence?

5

9

14

23

?

60

97

132 Using only the numbers and signs given, create a sum where both sides are equal.

What is it?

5, 7, 8, 9, 10, 11, +, +, x, x, =

133 On each row place a three-letter word that can be attached to the end of the word to the left and to the beginning of the word to the right, to give a longer word in each case.

When completed the initial letters of the 3-letter words will give a type of bird reading downwards. What is it?

SAUCE	_ _ _	CAKE
WEEK	_ _ _	OWED
KID	_ _ _	KIN
BUD	_ _ _	AWAY
AM	_ _ _	LESS
NOT	_ _ _	CAP
FISH	_ _ _	BALL

Mensa, the High IQ society

134 A clock was correct at midnight. From that moment it began to lose four minutes every hour.

The clock stopped 90 minutes ago, showing 15:52. What is the correct time? The clock runs for less than 24 hours.

Mensa, the High IQ society

135 A word can be attached to the beginning of all the given words to give six longer words. What is the word?

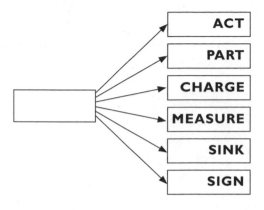

ACT

PART

CHARGE

MEASURE

SINK

SIGN

136 A quote by Eleanor Roosevelt has been split up into groups. Rearrange the groups to form the quote. What should it say?

AIRT HERS ITIS LING NOTF OASK OFOT RENO SELF TODO TWIL WHAT YOUA YOUR

137 Car A and Car B set off from the same point, at the same time, to travel the same journey. Car A travels at 48mph and Car B travels at 35mph.

If Car A stops after 140 miles, how long will it take for Car B to catch up?

138 How many miles should it be to Finland on this signpost?

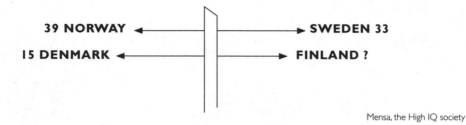

39 NORWAY ◄——————————► SWEDEN 33

15 DENMARK ◄——————————► FINLAND ?

Mensa, the High IQ society

139 A piggy bank contains £21.45. It is made up of four different denominations of coins and the largest denomination is £1. There is exactly the same number of each coin.

How many of each coin is there and what are their values?

Mensa, the High IQ society

140 The sum of each two adjacent blocks gives the number above. What number should replace the question mark?

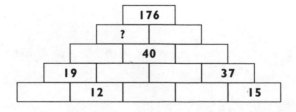

Mensa, the High IQ society

141 When each of the following words is rearranged, one of them can
be used to suffix the other five to give five longer words. What are the
five words?

PRIM   ROT   SON   ROPE   CALLS   LOB

Mensa, the High IQ society

142 What number should replace the question mark?

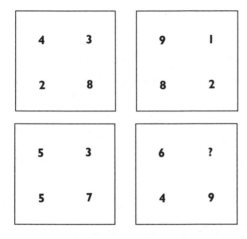

Mensa, the High IQ society

143 Martha Kearney has volunteered to mow the local village cricket ground.

She has a ride-on mower that cuts a strip that is 2 metres wide.
The ground is circular with a circumference of 400 metres.

She starts from the outside of the ground and goes around in ever-decreasing circles towards the centre.

Estimate the total distance she has travelled on her spiral journey.

Hugh Hunt, Reader in Engineering Dynamics and Vibration at Trinity College, Cambridge

144 A knight is positioned on the shaded square of this chessboard. Move the knight to each square once only, collecting letters to spell out four animals. What are they?

T	C	K	E	B
M	Y	A	A	N
A	E		M	K
A	O	W	O	P
Y	D	L	N	O

Mensa, the High IQ society

145 Martha plans to write (in English) all the whole numbers from zero to infinity in alphabetical order.

She knows this will take her a very long time, but she makes a start. She figures that first on her alphabetical list is the number eight.

What is the second number on her list?

After a while she tires of the task and jumps to the last page. She reckons that the last entry will be zero.

What is the second-last number on her alphabetical list?

Hugh Hunt, Reader in Engineering Dynamics and Vibration at Trinity College, Cambridge

146 John holds a solid cube in the sunshine (let's say the sun is directly overhead).

He holds it one metre above the ground and it casts a shadow.

He rotates the cube around a bit and finds that the smallest shadow he can create is a square.

What is the shape of the largest shadow he can produce with the cube and how much bigger is it than the square shadow?

Hugh Hunt, Reader in Engineering Dynamics and Vibration at Trinity College, Cambridge

147 WORLD MILK DAY

Raise a glass of milk to celebrate this dairy-themed puzzle!

Old McDonald had a farm, and on that farm he had a special cow called EIEIO who was renowned across the lands for her milk yields.

An evil rival farmer released 11 other robot cows that looked identical in every way to Old McDonald's prized cow EIEIO.

These 11 robot cows all weighed the same.

However, the cow EIEIO weighs either slightly more or less than the 11 robot cows.

Old McDonald needs to work out which is his prized cow EIEIO.

He has a set of cow balance scales that can either tell him if the scales are equal, or whether one side is heavier than the other.

There is a catch, however: he only has three chances to weigh the cows in any combination using the scales to find the prized cow EIEIO.

How would he do it?

Bobby Seagull, Cambridge University Doctorate student, school maths teacher
and author of *The Life Changing Magic of Numbers*

148 Martha asks John to think of a prime number bigger than three; for instance, he might choose seven.

She asks him to square it and subtract one, which in this case gives 48.

Martha remarks that 48 is divisible by 24.

Her challenge to John is to find a prime number bigger than three which, when squared and take away one, is NOT divisible by 24.

Are there any?

Hugh Hunt, Reader in Engineering Dynamics and Vibration at Trinity College, Cambridge

149 John and Martha are having a rolling race with four round objects on a gently sloping table.

John has a ping-pong ball and an empty aluminium can.

Martha has a billiard ball and a full jar of Vegemite (or peanut butter, if you prefer).

They line up the four objects at the top of the slope and let them roll down to the bottom. Who wins, and which object gets to the bottom fastest?

Hugh Hunt, Reader in Engineering Dynamics and Vibration at Trinity College, Cambridge

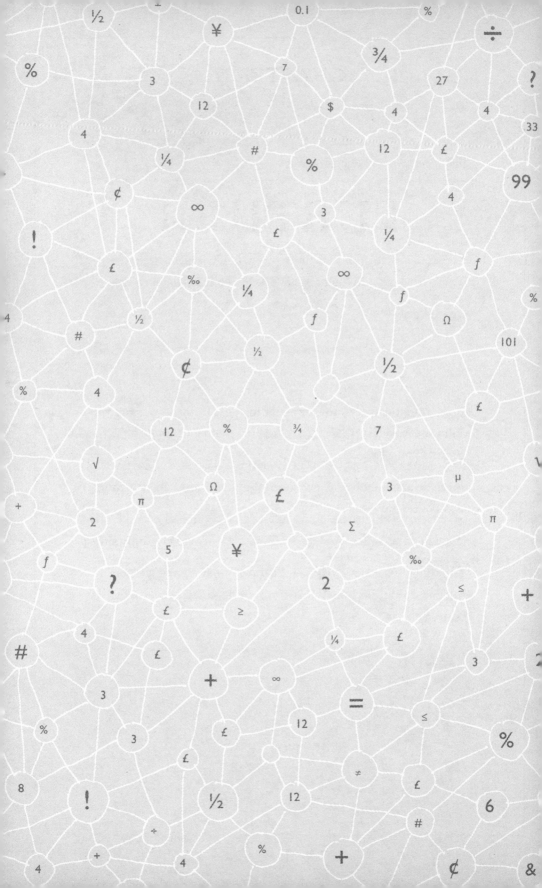

CHAPTER 4

FURTHER

MATHS

OK, you're going to need to know your integers from your square roots for some of these.

Having said that, they're not all as daunting as they look. **The Second-hand Car Salesman, Sam's Grandmother** and **The Court Astrologer** certainly shouldn't cause you too much grief.

And if you do get stuck, you can always ask a teenager currently sitting their GCSEs.

150 Do you know your integers?

$$a + b = c + d + e$$

$$a^2 + b^2 = c^2 + d^2 + e^2$$

What is the smallest set of unique integers, greater than zero, to satisfy these equations?

Paul Carden, Senior Lecturer in the Computer Science and Informatics Department, London South Bank University

151 **FIND THIS NUMBER:**

It's less than 100;

it's one more than a multiple of 3;

exactly one of the digits is prime;

if you reverse its digits, you get a prime number;

it has exactly four factors;

the sum of its digits is prime;

if you multiply it by 5, the answer is greater than 100.

University of Cambridge's NRICH project (nrich.maths.org), in collaboration with the UKMT

152 It's 2084 and Italy are hosting the Olympic Games. The IOC has commissioned a five-pizza dish to commemorate the occasion, based on the five continents of the globe and the iconic Olympic rings.

The Peoples Republic of Utopia, which is banned from the games for being too successful, has announced a 'World Championship' of their own, in protest. They have called for the creation of a pizza equal in area to the five-pizza Italian job.

However, the Pizza Association of Naples (PAN) have declared that a pizza's radius be measured in whole centimetres, not fractions of centimetres, to be officially recognised.

Why was this political move a masterstroke in thwarting Utopia's cunning culinary plan?

Paul Carden, Senior Lecturer in the Computer Science and Informatics Department,
London South Bank University

153 You have a new fish tank. Red guppies can only be bought in bags of five; whereas blue guppies come in bags of seven.

What's the minimum capacity of the tank, that is, the number of fish it can hold, which guarantees that the tank and all tanks of greater (integer) capacity can always be completely filled with a mixture of red and blue guppies?

School of Mathematics at The University of Manchester

154 You have two pound coins from the Isle of Man. You place both coins on a flat table and in contact with each other.

If you roll one coin completely around the outside of the other, maintaining contact between the coins, but not allowing any slippage, how many steps will the triskelion on the moving coin have taken?

School of Mathematics at The University of Manchester

155 If each letter represents a single digit, how many solutions are there to the sum:

BBC + NEWS = JOHN ?

School of Mathematics at The University of Manchester

156 **SAM'S GRANDMOTHER**

Sam asked her mother and grandmother how old they were. They each replied, 'My age in years is a square number.'

Her grandmother then added, 'The sum of our ages is also a square number.'

How old was Sam's grandmother?

UK Mathematics Trust (www.ukmt.org.uk)

157 Which fraction gives the same answer when it is subtracted from one-quarter as when it is multiplied by one-quarter?

UK Mathematics Trust (www.ukmt.org.uk)

158 All old Mother Hubbard had in her cupboard was a large pile of carrots. She gave each of her children one-twelfth of the carrots. She then found that one-third of the carrots were left over.

How many children did she have?

UK Mathematics Trust (www.ukmt.org.uk)

159 **THE SECOND-HAND CAR SALESMAN**

A used car salesman purchased a number of very old second-hand cars. He paid the same price of £325 for each car.

He has not yet sold all of the cars, but those that he has managed to sell each went for the giveaway price of £850.

If he has already made a profit of £8,975 and his car lot has room for no more than 50 cars at one time, how many cars remain?

Dr Steve Humble MBE, Head of Education, Newcastle University

160 Dan spins around a pole, initially at 33 revolutions per minute. With each revolution, his speed drops instantaneously by 11 rpms.

For how long does he spin?

Dr Gihan Marasingha, Senior Lecturer in Mathematics at the University of Exeter

161 When Alice's age is divided by 6, it leaves remainder 3. The remainder on division by 7 is 4.

What is the youngest that Alice could be?

Methuselah's age also has these properties but additionally leaves remainder 1 on division by 11.

What is the youngest Methuselah could be?

Dr Gihan Marasingha, Senior Lecturer in Mathematics at the University of Exeter

162 **THE COURT ASTROLOGER**

They let the court astrologer run the mint, and now the only currency is 9-plink and 17-plink coins.

If you are allowed to receive change, can you pay a bill for any number of plinks, or are some impossible?

What is the largest bill that you can't pay without needing change?

Professor Gregory Sankaran, Department for Mathematical Sciences at the University of Bath

163 My pizza was delivered unsliced. If I use two straight cuts, I can divide the pizza into four portions. I realise that three cunning cuts can create seven portions.

What is the maximum number of portions I can produce using ten straight cuts?

Dr Gihan Marasingha, Senior Lecturer in Mathematics at the University of Exeter

164 A TWO-PIPE PROBLEM

Two separate pipes, A and B, can feed water at a constant rate into a large water tank. Pipe A alone would fill an empty tank in 1 hour 20 minutes. Pipe B alone would fill an empty tank in 2 hours.

If both pipes were open at the same time, how long would it take to fill an empty tank?

School of Mathematics and Statistics at the University of Sheffield

165 WHAT IS MY PIN NUMBER?

I always had difficulty remembering my pin number until I noticed the following.

My house number has three digits and is different if I write it backwards. If I take the difference between my house number and its reverse I get another three-digit number.

If I add this new number to what I get if I reverse it, I get my (four-digit) pin-number.

It's secret because no one knows where I live. So what is my pin number?

Jonathan Mestel, Professor of Applied Mathematics, Imperial College London

166

Francesca the Frog is looking at a line of lily pads numbered 1, 2, 3, 4, 5, and so on.

She only jumps on lily pads with prime numbers.

For example, Francesca could jump on the prime lily pads 5, 11, 17, 23, 29. Those are five evenly spaced lily pads, the gap is 6 each time.

Can Francesca jump on five evenly spaced prime lily pads without using the lily pad 5?

Vicky Neale is the Whitehead Lecturer at the Mathematical Institute and Balliol College, Oxford

| 67 What prime property do the years 1994, 2005 and 2018 share?

When is the next year with this property?

Vicky Neale is the Whitehead Lecturer at the Mathematical Institute and Balliol College, University of Oxford

| 68 COME FLY WITH ME

Take an ordinary cotton reel with a hole down its axis through which air may pass. Hold it fixed with the hole vertical and place a piece of card horizontally immediately underneath it. If the card is released, it will fall to the floor, but by sucking through the hole, you should be able to hold the card in position.

What happens if instead of sucking you blow through the hole?

NOTE: When doing this in practice, it is a good idea to pass a drawing pin through the card so that its point rests loosely inside the hole. This gives the structure lateral stability while not affecting the vertical behaviour.

Jonathan Mestel, Professor of Applied Mathematics, Imperial College London

169 COVERING A CHESSBOARD WITH DOMINOES

There are many ways to cover an 8 × 8 chessboard with 32 two-by-one dominoes. But is it possible to use 31 dominoes to cover a modified chessboard which has had the two 'opposite' corner squares (for example, a1 and h8) removed?

Dr Daniel Mortlock, Lecturer in Astro-Statistics, Imperial College London and Guest Professor, Stockholm University

170 In a triangle, the difference, in degrees, between the largest angle and the middle angle is the same as the difference between the middle angle and the smallest angle. What is the middle angle in degrees?

UK Mathematics Trust (www.ukmt.org.uk)

171 Think of an inextensible rope going all the way around the Earth's equator.

Make it a nice snug fit.

Now, by inserting some extra rope, you make the rope two metres longer.

Two questions:

1. Suppose millions of little matchsticks were used to hold the rope up off the ground: how long do these matchsticks have to be to make the rope taut?

2. If instead you use one single tall tent pole to hold the rope up, how long does it have to be?

Hugh Hunt, Reader in Engineering Dynamics and Vibration at Trinity College, Cambridge

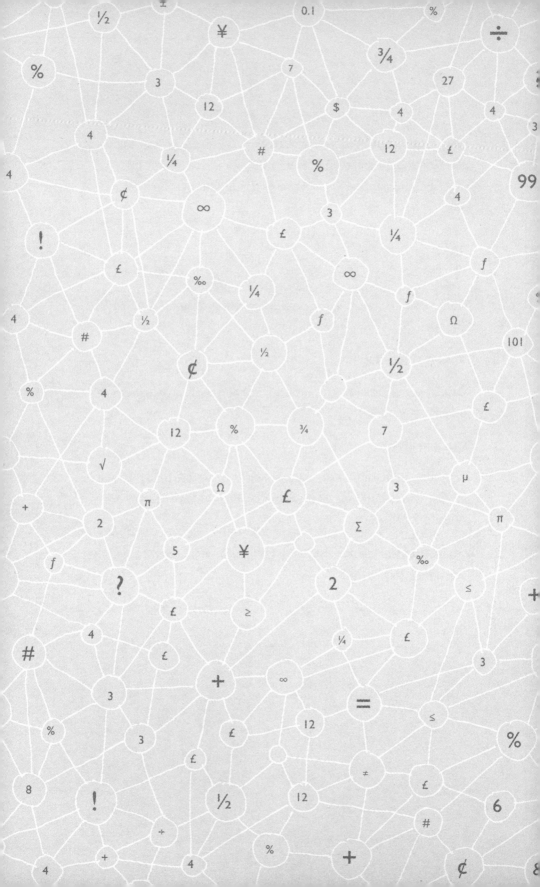

CHAPTER 5

NEW

PUZZLES

Inevitably we have built up quite a stockpile of puzzles that, at the time of compiling, haven't yet made it to air on the *Today* programme. There's no point in them sitting around in a drawer unsolved, so here's a selection to keep you going. Some of them will be broadcast in due course, so this is your chance to get ahead of the game.

Then, if you do hear one read out on air, you'll be able to shout out the answer quicker than John Humphrys can say 'eleven'.

172 In an unusual international conference, Europe is represented by
Serbia, Africa by Egypt, Asia by Kazakhstan and the Americas
by Mexico.

Why might this conference choose to exclude a representative from
Australasia?

Bobby Seagull, Cambridge University Doctorate student, school maths teacher
and author of *The Life Changing Magic of Numbers*

173 Let's engage your mind for numbers. What is next in this sequence?

3,
4,
6,
8,
12,
14,
18,
20
?

HINT: You don't need to be in your mental prime to solve this!

Bobby Seagull, Cambridge University Doctorate student, school maths teacher
and author of *The Life Changing Magic of Numbers*

174 What is the next number?

234,
4,916,
82,764,
?

Bobby Seagull, Cambridge University Doctorate student, school maths teacher
and author of *The Life Changing Magic of Numbers*

175 Mishal Husain, driving a red go-cart, and John Humphrys, driving a
blue go-cart, start moving in a circular track from the same spot, but in
opposite directions.

The track itself hasa circumference of 60km (it's a very big track!).
Mishal drives at 30km/hour while John at 20km/hour.

After how much time will the two cars meet?

Dr Georgiou, Senior Lecturer of Mathematics at the University of Sussex

176 What is next in the following sequence?

0104,
2104,
1204,
0404
?

HINT: Our American friends would have this sequence ordered slightly differently: 0401, 0421, 0412 but still 0404 for the last one.

Bobby Seagull, Cambridge University Doctorate student, school maths teacher
and author of *The Life Changing Magic of Numbers*

177 Why might a globe-trotting student visit the following countries on their travels in these particular months, especially if they're keen on parties:

Cambodia in November,
Kenya in December,
Australia in January,
Saint Lucia in February,
Greece in March,
Republic of Ireland in April
and Cuba in May.

Bobby Seagull, Cambridge University Doctorate student, school maths teacher
and author of *The Life Changing Magic of Numbers*

178 A particularly attentive traveller is planning their summer holidays and is thinking of going to the following countries in this particular order:

Jordan,
Algeria,
Ethiopia,
Ghana
and Nigeria.

Which country should be the final destination to maintain their attention to detail?

Bobby Seagull, Cambridge University Doctorate student, school maths teacher
and author of The Life Changing Magic of Numbers

179 **WORLDLY WOES**

Some newspaper headlines from the past:

'He robs US egg',
'Smash Sudan aid'
and finally 'Libya torn'

How are these international incidents linked by the 4th, 13th and 23rd letters of the alphabet?

Paul Carden, Senior Lecturer in the Computer Science and Informatics Department,
London South Bank University

180 SOMETHING TO DECLARE

A woman swam the channel from France to the UK every year for five years. At the end of that time she settled in the UK for good.

How was she able to accumulate seven passports?

Paul Carden, Senior Lecturer in the Computer Science and Informatics Department,
London South Bank University

181 CINEMA CLUES

Name the films:

TZZO,
TZZ,
FFO,
ONEF

Paul Carden, Senior Lecturer in the Computer Science and Informatics Department,
London South Bank University

182 SELF-DESTRUCTION

It is impossible for the star signs to align, and produce the study of their movements and relative positions. Why ?

Paul Carden, Senior Lecturer in the Computer Science and Informatics Department,
London South Bank University

183 **TIME TO TRAVEL**

I'm an American living in London and I'm the only one I know able to time-travel. On 30 October, I can celebrate Christmas Eve, on 31 October, I have my Christmas dinner and stay home all day with the family. On the 25 December, I can celebrate Halloween. On the 22 October I read *Frankenstein* cover to cover. But it's not always possible to move through time – only between 1 and 25 December and in October but never on a date with an 8 or 9 in it. The rest of the year my feet are firmly on the ground. How is this so?

Paul Carden, Senior Lecturer in the Computer Science and Informatics Department, London South Bank University

184 In our office of 24 people, 15 have a cat, 12 have a dog and 6 have a rabbit.

What is the minimum number of people who have at least 2 pets?

NRICH project (nrich.maths.org), University of Cambridge

185 A tram network has a circular route with 14 stops. On my regular journey home, I usually get off at the fifth stop, but yesterday I fell asleep and went round and round, through 37 stops altogether.

When I woke up, how many stops from home was I?

NRICH project (nrich.maths.org), University of Cambridge

186 On Christmas Day in 2017 the date was 25/12/17; this contains the digits 1, 2, 5 and 7 and no other digits.

If we use the date format of exactly two digits for the day, the month and the year, what will be the first date after this containing the digits 1, 2, 5 and 7 with no other digits appearing?

Daniel Griller, mathematics teacher, Olympiad problem composer, and author of the puzzle book *Elastic Numbers*

187 What percentage of the possible three-letter combinations in the modern Roman alphabet are words in English?

School of Mathematics at The University of Manchester

188 The January exams are over, and a report has to be written for every student. With the deadline looming, one teacher realises that if they start immediately, they must write an average of four reports a day to be finished on time; if, however, they start tomorrow, they will have to write an average of four and a half reports a day.

How many students do they have?

Daniel Griller, mathematics teacher, Olympiad problem composer, and author of the puzzle book *Elastic Numbers*

189 A tourist starts at one end of a train line, travels all the way to the other end of the line and all the way back again.

There are ten stations on the line, and by the end of the day, the tourist has taken one photo at each station.

In how many different orders could the photos have been taken?

Daniel Griller, mathematics teacher, Olympiad problem composer, and author of the puzzle book *Elastic Numbers*

190 Today I noticed that the odometer on my car showed 59865 miles, which reads the same whether I look at it the right way up or upside down. I bought the car second-hand with 30,000 miles on the clock.

How many times since then has this occurred?

NRICH project (nrich.maths.org), University of Cambridge

191 My postcard collection contains some 4 inch by 3 inch 'landscape' postcards, and some 3 inch by 4 inch 'portrait' postcards.

I have a large sheet of paper, 21 inches by 18 inches.

What is the maximum number of postcards I can fit on the sheet?

NRICH project (nrich.maths.org), University of Cambridge

192 At the cycling festival, everyone brings their bicycle or tricycle for a fun day out. I counted 50 people altogether, but there were 117 wheels.

How many people brought a bicycle?

NRICH project (nrich.maths.org), University of Cambridge

193 How many regular tetrahedrons (regular solids with four triangular faces) can be placed inside a single larger tetrahedron formed by doubling the length of all edges of one of the original tetrahedrons?

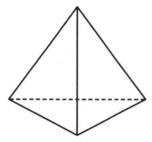

School of Mathematics at The University of Manchester

194 You have 100 5-ml samples of blood and know that up to nine could be carrying a particularly nasty disease.

Luckily, there is a test for the disease that requires only 1ml of diseased blood.

What is the maximum number of tests that must be performed to identify all diseased samples?

School of Mathematics at The University of Manchester

195 Which UK coin has the greater volume: 2p or 50p?

School of Mathematics at The University of Manchester

196 You have a length of cable that is 10cm long, with a diameter of 1cm. Is it possible to tie a knot in it?

School of Mathematics at The University of Manchester

197 Stentorian crickets will always emit a short chirp if they hear the chirp of another cricket.

Assuming that there is an 80 per cent chance that any individual cricket hears the chirp of another cricket in the group, how large a group of crickets will ensure a less than 1 per cent chance that the chirping stops once started by a single cricket?

School of Mathematics at The University of Manchester

198 How many different ways are there to combine two 2 × 4 plastic building bricks of different colours?

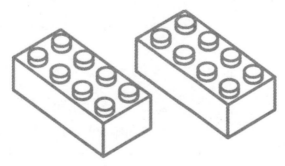

School of Mathematics at The University of Manchester

199 You want to plant three trees in a square field so that they are as far away as possible from each other.

Where should you plant them?

School of Mathematics at The University of Manchester

200 MINOTAUR MAZE

As you walk through a maze, you have to make decisions to take the right or left path. On the way to the exit you need to make six of these decisions.

What is the chance you will take the correct path?

Dr Steve Humble MBE, Head of Education, Newcastle University

201 Anna, Bethany and Charlotte have been on an Easter egg hunt. Charlotte has found one more egg than Anna, but lucky Bethany has found three times as many as Anna. If Bethany were to eat one of hers, she would have twice as many eggs as Charlotte.

How many eggs does Anna have?

Dr Steve Humble MBE, Head of Education, Newcastle University

202 Two players place 15 coins in front of them. Each then takes one, two or three coins on their turn. The winner is the player with an odd number of coins at the end of the game. For example, if you end up with seven and your opponent has eight, you win.

How many coins should the first player take on his first turn to guarantee winning?

Dr Steve Humble MBE, Head of Education, Newcastle University

203 Rebecca, Harry and Juliet have been given 54 small chocolate Easter eggs. The eggs are to be divided up in the following way:

Every time Rebecca gets two eggs,
Harry gets three
and Juliet gets one less than Harry and Rebecca combined.

How many eggs does Harry get?

Dr Steve Humble MBE, Head of Education, Newcastle University

204 Any man who bites me feels my bite. I appear between equal head and tail. Flay me and I grow in strength. You, my jailer, reveal my name.

Dr Gihan Marasingha, Senior Lecturer in mathematics at the University of Exeter

205 Moses decides to build a tabernacle with a base that is a right-angled triangle. He insists that the square of the longest side must be at least a thousand square cubits and that the squares of the other two sides must each be less than a thousand square cubits.

What possibilities exist for the lengths of the sides?

Dr Gihan Marasingha, Senior Lecturer in mathematics at the University of Exeter

206 On the first day of Christmas, I received one gift from my true love: a partridge in a pear tree.

On the second day, I received three gifts: a partridge, and two turtle doves.

In total, over the 12 days, how many gifts did I receive?

Dr Gihan Marasingha, Senior Lecturer in mathematics at the University of Exeter

207 Having over-indulged at Christmas, Mr and Mrs Claus decide to burn the fat with competitive exercise. They race each other over 100m.

In the first race, Mrs Claus wins handily by 20m. Mr Claus asks his wife if she would begin 20m behind the start line on the next race. She obliges.

Assuming they run at a constant speed, who wins the second race?

Dr Gihan Marasingha, Senior Lecturer in mathematics at the University of Exeter

208 An ant crawls on the surface of a vertical cylinder, 6cm in circumference and 4cm high.

She starts at a point on the bottom edge of the cylinder and wishes to reach the diametrically opposite point on the top edge of the cylinder.

What is the length of the shortest route between these two points?

Dr Gihan Marasingha, Senior Lecturer in mathematics at the University of Exeter

209 NUMBER OF PRIMES

The lowest prime numbers are 2, 3, 5, 7, 11 and so on (the number 1 is not considered prime).

The number of primes thins out quite dramatically when you go higher – there are 25 primes between 0 and 100, 16 primes between 1,000 and 1,100, just 11 between 10,000 and 10,100.

But do they run out altogether or are there infinitely many? And how can you be sure?

Dr Daniel Mortlock, Lecturer in Astro-Statistics, Imperial College London
and Guest Professor, Stockholm University

210 In WWII, the Americans faced the problem of reinforcing their bomber planes. Reinforcing all parts of the plane would make them heavy, meaning that they wouldn't be as agile and would also use a lot of fuel. Consider that the four main parts of the plane are the cockpit, engines, fuselage and wings.

If your returning planes all have bullet holes in the fuselage and the wings, which parts of the plane should you reinforce?

Dr Jennifer Rogers, The Royal Statistical Society and Department of Statistics, University of Oxford

211 Jeremy Corbyn boards a train to Newcastle and, having learned from past mistakes, has reserved himself one of the 500 seats.

Unfortunately, he is the last to board, and finds every other passenger has sat in seats at random, leaving one seat free.

Determined to take only the seat reserved in his name, what is the probability Jeremy won't have to sit on the floor?

Dr Jennifer Rogers, The Royal Statistical Society and Department of Statistics, University of Oxford

212 A RECURRING PROBLEM

What fraction, in lowest terms, gives the recurring decimal number 3.6 followed by the digits 342 repeated forever, that is

3.6342342342 etc.?

School of Mathematics and Statistics at the University of Sheffield

213 AN INTERESTING NUMBER

I inflate one of two identical spotted balloons until all its spots are an inch across, and the other until all its spots are a foot across.

Now I join the necks of the balloons, letting air flow from one into the other, pinching them off again when the spots on the larger balloon have decreased to 10 inches across.

How big now are the spots on the other balloon?

School of Mathematics and Statistics at the University of Sheffield

214 JUST AROUND THE CORNER

Can an equilateral triangle be covered by two smaller equilateral triangles?

School of Mathematics and Statistics at the University of Sheffield

215 CONNECT FIVE

Which famous trilogy connects the following five words?

**monkeys,
city,
northwest,
summer,
comfort**

School of Mathematics and Statistics at the University of Sheffield

216 Why does mayonnaise buck the trend in the following list of words?

**lime,
common,
ilk,
way,
water,
lout**

School of Mathematics and Statistics at the University of Sheffield

217 I am given 12 coins labelled A to L. 11 of them are the same weight, but one of them is not, and I do not know if it is heavy or light.

I am given an ordinary balance and three weighings to determine which is the fake coin and whether it is heavy or light.

On each weighing, the labels on the coins in each scale pan must spell a common English word. How do I do this?

School of Mathematics and Statistics at the University of Sheffield

218 Your friend hands you six matches and asks whether you can arrange the matches to form exactly four equilateral triangles. Can you do it?

School of Mathematics and Statistics at the University of Sheffield

219 What connects the following seven words?

knees,
eyes,
breakfast,
years,
mouth,
share,
ear

School of Mathematics and Statistics at the University of Sheffield

220 **EASY AS PIE**

A toddler playing with blocks lays out the row

A mathematician sees the arrangement and gasps when the child adds a ninth block.

What was the ninth block, and what was the sequence?

School of Mathematics and Statistics at the University of Sheffield

221 The Easter bunny has hidden 250 boxes in his magic garden, each one containing an Easter egg. Children visit the garden, one by one, to look for boxes and they get to take away the egg inside the first box they find, leaving an empty box behind. 11 children are visiting the bunny today, one after the other.

What's the chance that at least one of them will be disappointed to find an empty box?

Institute and Faculty of Actuaries

222 What should the next pair of numbers be?

3 and 7;
5 and 11;
11 and 23;
23 and 47;
29 and 59;
?

Professor Gregory Sankaran, Department for Mathematical Sciences at the University of Bath

223 A shop manager wants to put a sign in the window saying MERRY XMAS, in capital letters.

The manager gives three of the letters, at random, to each of his three assistants and tells them to put them up. They put them in the right order, and two of the assistants put their letters up the right way, but the third assistant is just as likely to put a letter upside down, or backwards, or both, as the right way.

How likely is it that the message nevertheless comes out right?

Professor Gregory Sankaran, Department for Mathematical Sciences at the University of Bath

224 The World Mornington Crescent Champion is playing a match against a challenger. The first player to win six games becomes champion, but if the score is five wins each, the match is drawn and the champion keeps the title. In fact the two players are equally good, so equally likely to win any single game.

How likely is it that the challenger becomes champion?

Professor Gregory Sankaran, Department for Mathematical Sciences at the University of Bath

225 In a given month, the probability of a certain daily paper's either running a story about inappropriate behaviour at a party conference OR running one about somebody's pet being retrieved from a domestic appliance (but never running both) is exactly half the probability of the same paper's containing a photo of a Tory MP jogging.

The probability of no such photo appearing is the same as that of there being a story about inappropriate behaviour at a party conference.

The probability of the paper's running a story about somebody's pet being retrieved from a domestic appliance is a quarter that of its containing a photo of a Tory MP jogging.

What are the probabilities the paper will
(a) run the conference story,
(b) run the pet story,
(c) contain the jogging photo?

Dr Roger Teichmann, Lecturer in Philosophy, St Hilda's College, University of Oxford

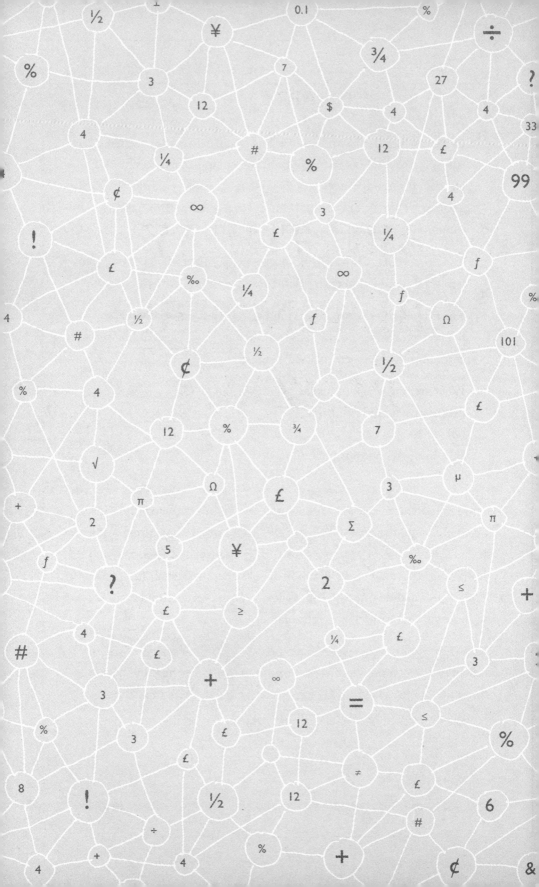

CHAPTER 6

BBC *TODAY* PRESENTERS' PUZZLES

A number of our puzzle setters have gone out of their way to build their puzzles around the personalities of the *Today* programme presenters. In some cases this is a simple substitution – instead of Rita, Sue and Bob Too, we have some combination of John, Sarah, Mishal, Justin and Nick. Jim Naughtie gets a look in, as do one or two others, but I can't say more about that without giving the game away.

Elsewhere the puzzle setters have made a more concerted effort to reflect the presenters' character or on-air persona. You might very well think that John's chagrin at being served a smaller pizza than Sarah is revealing; I couldn't possibly comment.

226 A maths magician says to John Humphrys:

'Think of a number. Double it.

Add **8**.

Multiply by **5**.

Subtract **24** and then tell me your result.'

John says '**56**'

The magician is now able to quickly calculate the number John was initially thinking of.

What is that number?
And how does the magician know?

Dr Steve Humble MBE, Head of Education, Newcastle University

227 The six *Today* programme presenters have gathered for Christmas lunch. The BBC caterers have miscounted, and have only provided five mince pies.

In how many ways can the presenters share the five mince pies among themselves?

Vicky Neale, Whitehead Lecturer at the Mathematical Institute and Balliol College, University of Oxford

228 THE ART GALLERY PROBLEM

The BBC is about to move into new premises and the Head of Security wants to install security cameras so that all areas of the building are covered.

Following a mix-up in communications, the floorplan of the building is not known, but the single-storey building is completely open plan with **fifty** straight walls.

What is the minimum number of cameras that are guaranteed to be sufficient?

School of Mathematics at the University of Manchester

229 If Mishal is **9**,
Nick is **10**,
and both Sarah and Justin are **11**,
what is John?

Bobby Seagull, Cambridge University Doctorate student, school maths teacher and author of The Life Changing Magic of Numbers

230 A maths magician says to James Naughtie:

'Remove the court cards (Kings, Queens and Jacks) from a deck of cards. Select a card from **1** to **10**.
Double the value of the card.
Add **3**.
Multiply by **5**.
If the card selected is a club, add **1**.
If it is a diamond, add **2**.
If it is a heart, add **3** and
if a spade, add **4**.

Now tell me your answer.'

James says, '**79**'

The magician is now able to quickly calculate the card James selected.

What is that card? And how does the magician know?

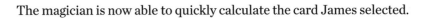

Dr Steve Humble MBE, Head of Education, Newcastle University

231 A maths magician says to Sarah Montague:

'Pick a number.
Add **7**.
Multiply the result by **9**.
Now add **13**.
Add up the digits in your answer.

'If the number you obtain contains more than one digit, add the digits again. Continue doing this until you obtain a one-digit result.'

Regardless of which number Sarah initially picked, the final one-digit number is always the same.

What is that number? And how does the magician know?

Dr Steve Humble MBE, Head of Education, Newcastle University

232 A maths magician says to Nick Robinson:

'Write down any number.
Scramble the digits to make another number.
Subtract the smaller of the two numbers from the larger.
Circle any non-zero digit in the result.
Add the remaining digits and tell me the total answer of the sum.'

Nick says, '**16**'.

The magician is now able to quickly calculate the number Nick circled.

What is that number? And how does the magician know?

Dr Steve Humble MBE, Head of Education, Newcastle University

233 PRESENTING A PROBLEM

What is the next character in the following sequence?

E,

5,

A,

N,

500,

A,

5,

1,

?

School of Mathematics and Statistics at the University of Sheffield

234 JUST-IN-TIME

Later this century, not long before retirement age, Justin Webb will turn x squared years old in the year y squared.

Which year was Justin born in?

School of Mathematics and Statistics at the University of Sheffield

235 JOHN'S MAGIC NUMBER

Sarah Montague and John Humphrys go for pizza.

When the pizzas arrive, the circumference of Sarah's is **61cm**, while that of John's is only **60cm**.

John orders a second, customised mini-pizza to make up the exact difference in pizza size.

What is its circumference, in centimetres?

School of Mathematics and Statistics at the University of Sheffield

236

Martha Kearney and Nick Robinson have a reading competition for the ten days of the Hay Festival, the annual literature festival. Martha reads one page on the first day, then doubles to read two pages on the second day and then doubles again to read four pages on the third day.

She keeps doing this, doubling her reading pages each day, so after three days Martha has read 1 + 2 + 4, a total of seven pages.

Nick has a different reading strategy. Nick starts by reading 10 pages on day one, then 20 pages on day two, then 30 pages on day three and so on, increasing his reading by 10 pages each day. So after three days, Nick has read 10 + 20 + 30, a total of 60 pages.

After how many days does Martha read more pages in total than Nick?

Bobby Seagull, Cambridge University Doctorate student, school maths teacher
and author of *The Life Changing Magic of Numbers*

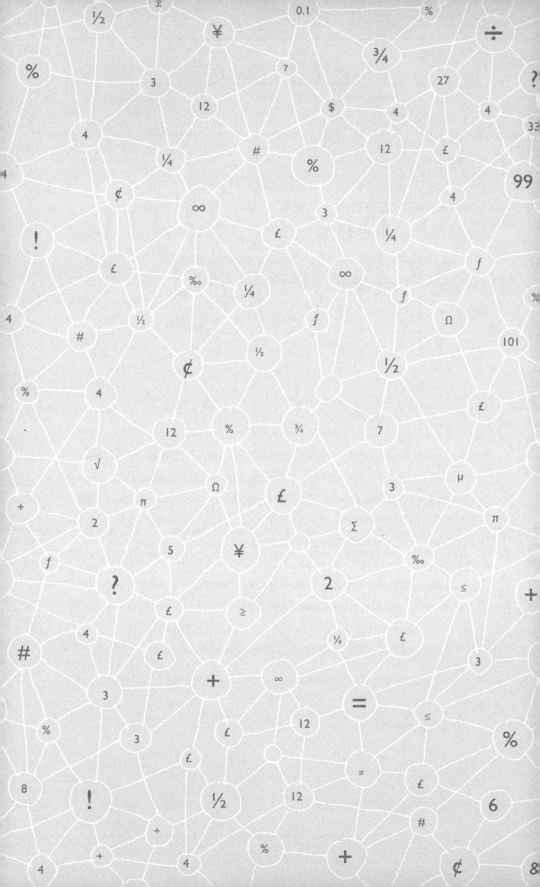

CHAPTER 7

CELEBRITY

SETTERS

The term 'celebrity' probably needs some explanation here. We're not talking about passing film stars or senior politicians who thought it might be fun to get involved and asked their PA to think of a puzzle. The questions featured here are all set by well-known mathematicians and puzzle setters who liked what we were doing and wanted to get involved. Many have published their own collections or books on puzzling, and all agreed to appear on the programme to set a #PuzzleForToday.

237 A rectangular piece of paper has sides that are **25cm** and **36cm** long.

Cut the paper with a pair of scissors in a single, continuous line, such that the two cut pieces can be put together to make a square.

How do you do it?

Alex Bellos, puzzle blogger at the *Guardian* and author

238 A palindrome is an expression that reads the same forwards and back.

A palindrome time is a time – expressed in hours, minutes and seconds – that is the same forwards and back, like 3:59:53.

There are 660 palindrome times using a 24-hour clock.

Which two palindrome times are the closest together?

Nobuyuki Yoshigahara, selected by Alex Bellos, author of *Puzzle Ninja: Pit Your Wits Against The Japanese Puzzle Masters*

239 Find A and B when both A and B are palindromes – that is, numbers that read the same forwards and back – and $A + B = 12345$

Naoki Inaba, selected by Alex Bellos, author of *Puzzle Ninja: Pit Your Wits Against the Japanese Puzzle Masters*

240 My British friend James Jason works as a disc jockey at the BBC,
where his programme is broadcast on both FM and AM at the
same time.

His business card says:

J Jason
DJ
FM/AM

I've found a pattern in his card.

What is it?

Nobuyuki Yoshigahara, selected by Alex Bellos, author of *Puzzle Ninja:
Pit Your Wits Against The Japanese Puzzle Masters*

241   John says that Justin is a liar.

Justin says that Tom is a liar.

Tom says that Justin and John are liars.

Who is telling the truth?

CLARIFICATION: For the purposes of this puzzle, all persons involved either always tell the truth, or always lie.

Alex Bellos, puzzle blogger at the *Guardian* and author

242   The main draw for the Wimbledon men's or ladies' tennis championship has **128** entrants.

If we quadrupled the number of entrants in the draw to **512**, how many matches would there have to be in the traditional knockout format for there to be a winner?

Bobby Seagull, Cambridge University Doctorate student, school maths teacher
and author of *The Life Changing Magic of Numbers*

243 Take a journey on the London Underground using the following lines in this particular order:

Central,
London Overground,
Circle,
District,
Piccadilly.

Why might a history (or science) teacher feel this journey is incomplete?

Bobby Seagull, Cambridge University Doctorate student, school maths teacher
and author of *The Life Changing Magic of Numbers*

244 It happened in the beginning and the 2nd time.

It then happened again on the 8th time.

It then happened on the 10th and 11th time and it most recently happened on the 16th time (it did not happen on the 21st time in 2018).

What are we referring to?

Bobby Seagull, Cambridge University Doctorate student, school maths teacher
and author of *The Life Changing Magic of Numbers*

245 2, 2, 1, 5, 11, 12, 4, 1, 6, 3, 2, 10, 2, 1, 4, 7, 4, 2, 2, 4, 2, 1

What is the next number?

HINT: Channel your inner Jane Austen as you will have to swallow your pride and show no opening bias when attempting to answer this.

Bobby Seagull, Cambridge University Doctorate student, school maths teacher
and author of *The Life Changing Magic of Numbers*

246 POETRY-BASED PUZZLE

Two plus two is four minus one that's three,

So solving this riddle will set you free.

If waking up at dawn is a struggle,

Then surely so might cracking this puzzle.

To start, a city with Indiana Jones's holy grail,

Another time, leader of the Argonauts did not fail.

Once the author of the Modern Prometheus, oh strife,

Most recently Godfather of punk with a lust for life.

Here's one problem we made earlier, so this is a clue,

What on earth are we talking about, do not turn to blue.

Bobby Seagull, Cambridge University Doctorate student, school maths teacher
and author of *The Life Changing Magic of Numbers*

247 SIX MANIACS

Moriarty has trapped Sherlock in a maze with six crazy assassins. The entrance has been blocked off and we may assume that any encounters that happen are between a pair.

They all circulate and each of them is as likely to meet any one of the others.

Sherlock is unarmed, and the assassins are crazy: if he meets one of the assassins, our hero will definitely perish; if two assassins meet, they will eliminate each other.

Before this game starts, the evil Moriarty makes a generous offer to reduce the number of assassins by one.

Should Sherlock accept?

What are his chances of survival?

Chris Maslanka, British writer and broadcaster, specialising in puzzles and problem solving, and Enigmatist of St Catherine's College, Oxford

248 While the following sequence of numbers may look of a mathematical nature, a mindset of *Citius, altius, fortius* may help unlock the keys.

What number comes next?

1,
2,
4,
8,
15,
50
?

Bobby Seagull, Cambridge University Doctorate student, school maths teacher and author of The Life Changing Magic of Numbers

249 Let's take a giant step across the pond that is the Atlantic Ocean and go to the United States.

Hiram, Stephen, Thomas, John, James and William are part of an exclusive, and perhaps slightly less formal, American club.

What connects them?

Bobby Seagull, Cambridge University Doctorate student, school maths teacher and author of The Life Changing Magic of Numbers

250 'In virtual Xeroxing, letters can dimly manifest.'

Why might this prove useful if you were visiting monuments such as the Colosseum, the Pantheon or the Circus Maximus?

Bobby Seagull, Cambridge University Doctorate student, school maths teacher
and author of *The Life Changing Magic of Numbers*

251 Find the number $ABCD$ such that $ABCD \times 9 = DCBA$.

Tetsuya Miyamoto, selected by Alex Bellos, author of *Puzzle Ninja:
Pit Your Wits Against The Japanese Puzzle Masters*

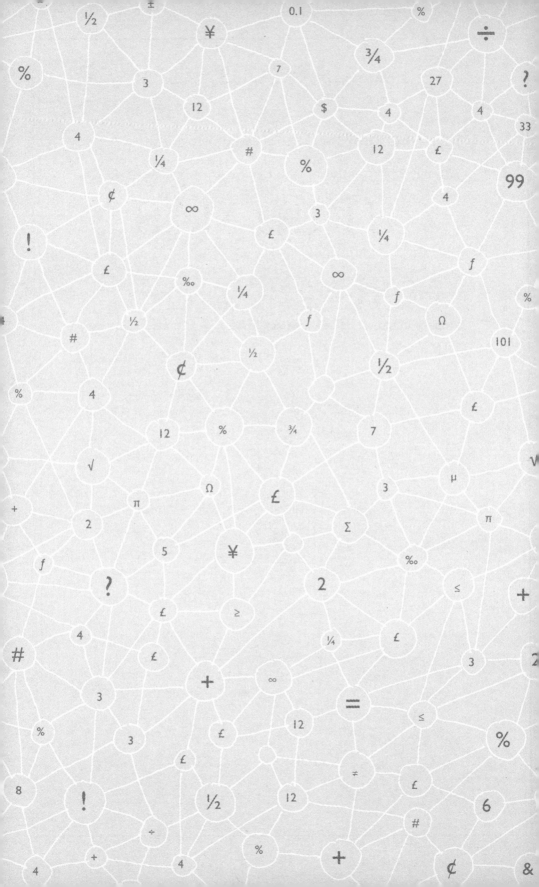

CHAPTER 8

CHRISTMAS

CRACKERS

December seemes to offer the perfect opportunity for some themed puzzling. All the Christmas favourites are here, the reindeer, presents, partridges in pear trees, cheese and pineapple squares on cocktail sticks, snow, Scrooge and, of course, Father Christmas and the elves.

This was the programme's #PuzzleForToday Advent calendar.

252 Father Christmas always celebrates his birthday by waking up at sunrise and going for a walk.

This year he was staying at his home in the Arctic.

When he woke up, he walked ten miles south, ten miles east and ten miles north, only to find himself back where he started.

When is his birthday?

Alex Bellos, puzzle blogger at the *Guardian* and author

253 A partridge in a pear tree and a pair of turtle doves are worth five reindeer. Similarly, three partridges in a pear tree and two pairs of turtle doves are worth 12 reindeer.

How much is a partridge in a pear tree worth?

Bobby Seagull, Cambridge University Doctorate student, school maths teacher and author of *The Life Changing Magic of Numbers*

254 You are preparing cheese and pineapple sticks to serve at your Christmas party.

You have a big cube of cheese and need to cut it into **27** small cubes.

What is the smallest number of cuts you need to make?

HINT: you are allowed to rearrange the slices after each cut if you wish.

Alex Bellos, puzzle blogger at the *Guardian* and author

255 Santa Claus delivers presents to children who have been nice throughout the world in this particular order:
Bulgaria,
Jordan,
Bahamas,
Japan,
Greece.

He stops for some mince pies and then continues with:
Denmark,
Peru,
Turkey,
Mongolia.

What country might he visit next?

Bobby Seagull, Cambridge University Doctorate student, school maths teacher
and author of *The Life Changing Magic of Numbers*

256 In the Radio Four *Today* programme's Secret Santa for exchanging gifts,

Mishal gets a calendar,

Justin gets a clock,

Sarah gets some shoes

and Nick gets a scarf.

What might John receive?

Bobby Seagull, Cambridge University Doctorate student, school maths teacher
and author of *The Life Changing Magic of Numbers*

257 Santa, Mrs Claus and Santa's eight reindeer all buy each other a Christmas present from **'ELFridges**.

How many presents in total are there under the tree?

Hywel Carver, author of *Sodding Sums: The 10% of Maths You Actually Need*

258 Santa is buying Christmas crackers for Christmas dinner with nine guests (so ten people in total).

He wants to buy enough so that everyone can pull a cracker with each other person at dinner.

How many does he need?

Hywel Carver, author of *Sodding Sums: The 10% of Maths You Actually Need*

259 The snow outside Santa's front door is 40cm deep and, as it's getting colder, it's getting 50 per cent deeper every day.

How deep will it be in three days' time?

Hywel Carver, author of *Sodding Sums: The 10% of Maths You Actually Need*

260 Ebenezer Scrooge hates to join the Cratchit family's Secret Santa unless he receives a present that's worth more than the present he buys.

There are eight other people in the Secret Santa:

Bob Cratchit, Mrs Cratchit and the six Cratchit children.

Each of the Cratchit children will spend all their pocket money (1p) on a lollipop for whomever they get, like they do every year.

Mrs Cratchit will spend 16p on wool and knit a scarf for whomever she gets, and Bob will *either* buy a 2p lollipop *or*, with equal probability, a toy boat for 12p.

Scrooge will always buy a 5p lump of coal.

What is the probability that Scrooge is going to get a present worth more than the present he buys?

Hywel Carver, author of *Sodding Sums: The 10% of Maths You Actually Need*

26 | Nicholas has purchased three identical cheeseboards, four identical Christmas puddings and six identical boxes of chocolate.

He must use all the items to fill 2 Christmas hampers, one large and one small.

Each hamper must contain at least one item of each type, and the large hamper must contain more items than the small hamper.

In how many different ways can he fill the hampers?

Daniel Griller, mathematics teacher, Olympiad problem composer
and author of the puzzle book Elastic Numbers

262   BEER + BEER = $DRUNK$

A maths equation for the festive season.

If each letter represents a different digit, your challenge is to discover which digit each letter represents.

Dr Steve Humble MBE, Head of Education, Newcastle University

263 A Christmas tree is decorated with 36 lights, which are ordered one through to 36. Timers are set so that every five minutes a change occurs in the light pattern. The sequence of changes repeats every three hours. Light switches are set so that:

At the end of the first five minutes, every light is turned on.

At the end of the second five minutes, every second light switch is reversed and therefore switched off.

At the end of the third five minutes, every third light switch is reversed and therefore if it was switched on it is then switched off and vice versa.

At the end of the fourth five minutes, every fourth light switch is reversed and so on for all of the three hours.

Which lights are switched on during the final five-minute interval before the whole sequence repeats itself?

Dr Steve Humble MBE, Head of Education, Newcastle University

264 You have two Christmas candles, each with wicks at both ends. If any one of the four wicks is lit, the lit candle will burn out at a non-uniform rate in exactly one hour.

Can you time 45 minutes using the two candles and some matches?

School of Mathematics and Statistics at the University of Sheffield

265 A family gave their children £7 to spend at the shops. In the shop there are three sizes of special Christmas sweets:

one for £1,

two for £1,

and three for £1.

The family has as many boys as girls. If each child gets exactly the same number and kinds of sweets, how many sweets of each size does each child receive?

Dr Steve Humble MBE, Head of Education, Newcastle University

266 *The Wizard of Oz* lasts 1 hour and 40 minutes. *The Great Escape* lasts 2 hours and 50 minutes. Starting at 10am on Christmas Eve, two friends watch one film each, on a loop. They stop watching when the films finish at exactly the same time.

Will they miss the Queen's speech?

School of Mathematics and Statistics at the University of Sheffield

267 For a Christmas party, 20 people went to a restaurant for a meal.

The bill came to £600, so they shared the bill and paid £30 each.

Just before they were about to leave, the restaurant owner realised he had made an error and had overcharged the group by £50. The owner asked the waiter to return the £50 to the 20 customers.

Unfortunately the waiter was none too honest. He realised that, since £50 is not exactly divisible by 20, that he would keep £10 and return £40 to the group, so that each would get £2 back (and hopefully leave a bigger tip!). This means that each person only paid £28.

20 times 28 is £560, plus the waiter's £10 makes £570.

What happened to the missing £30?

Dr Steve Humble MBE, Head of Education, Newcastle University

268 A bakery has prepared a batch of mince pies.

The first customer to the store purchases three-quarters for a Christmas party that evening.

The second customer takes half of the remaining, then buys seven more for a friend.

The third customer takes the last nine of the batch.

How many were there to start with?

Tes, which hosts a full curriculum of maths lessons developed in collaboration with White Rose Maths, available free on its resources site

269 Santa is beginning to think about the best way to organise his reindeer into a team. He has eight reindeer:

Dasher,
Dancer,
Prancer,
Vixen,
Comet,
Cupid,
Donner
and Blitzen.

He wants to arrange them into four rows of reindeer, with two reindeer in each row. Unfortunately, the reindeer are picky. Donner and Vixen hate each other and cannot be in the same row. Comet and Vixen must be in the same column. Donner and Blitzen are good friends and must either be in the same row or they must be in the same column with one directly in front of the other.

In how many ways can Santa team up his reindeer?

Dr Gihan Marasingha, Senior Lecturer in mathematics at the University of Exeter

270 On Christmas Day I start giving away all the gifts that my true love sent to me, at the rate of one gift per day.

Will I have any gifts left on the following Christmas Day?

School of Mathematics and Statistics at the University of Sheffield

271 On the first day of Christmas, my true love sent to me: a partridge in a pear tree.

On the second day of Christmas, my true love sent to me: two turtle doves and a partridge in a pear tree.

And so my true love persisted in this unnecessarily generous fashion, all the way to the twelfth day of Christmas, when my true love sent to me: **12** drummers drumming, **11** pipers piping, **10** lords a leaping, **9** ladies dancing, **8** maids a milking, **7** swans a swimming, **6** geese a laying, **5** gold rings, **4** calling birds, **3** French hens, **2** turtle doves and a partridge in a pear tree.

On what day did I receive my 100th present, and what was it?

NOTE: For the avoidance of doubt, the gifts were received in the order listed in the song.

Vicky Neale, Whitehead Lecturer at the Mathematical Institute and Balliol College, University of Oxford

272 **CHRISTMAS CRUCIVERBALISM**

A Christmas cruciverbalist is puzzled by the following clue:

'Mulled wine thinker blamed it on Carol'.

Can you help them solve it?

School of Mathematics and Statistics at the University of Sheffield

273 HANDS TIED TOGETHER

You arrive at a party with your Christmas jumper accidentally on inside out. Your host is furious and ties your hands together before you can fix your jumper.

Can you lessen your host's rage by putting your jumper on the right way around while your hands are tied together?

School of Mathematics and Statistics at the University of Sheffield

274

You receive six books as Christmas gifts. You get exactly one book about Rudolf, and one about cookery. You decide that these two books should not appear side by side on your shelf.

How many different ways can your six new books be arranged on your shelf?

School of Mathematics and Statistics at the University of Sheffield

275 A stallholder at a school Christmas fair is offering cash prizes in a game to raise funds for the school.

He has a bag of six balls, half of which are green and the other half red. For a donation to the school, players draw three balls out of the bag at random, sight unseen. For each player who draws all three green balls, the stallholder will double their money.

What is the chance of a player winning a prize?

Institute and Faculty of Actuaries

276 A farmer brings 400 turkeys and geese to a Christmas market to sell.

Three-quarters of the turkeys and one-third of the geese are sold. There are 125 turkeys and geese left in total.

How many turkeys were sold?

Tes, which hosts a full curriculum of maths lessons developed in collaboration with White Rose Maths, available free on its resources site

277 You have a cup of eggnog and a glass of brandy. You put a teaspoon of eggnog in the brandy and mix it up, then you put a teaspoon of this mixture back into the eggnog cup.

Is there more eggnog in the brandy glass or brandy in the eggnog cup?

Dr Kit Yates, Senior Lecturer in Mathematics at the Centre for Mathematical Biology in the Department for Mathematical Sciences at the University of Bath

278 An office orders 110 bottles of red and white wine in total for its Christmas party. A third of the bottles of red wine are drunk and 20 of the white. There are now the same number of each remaining for employees to take home.

How many bottles of red were there to start with?

Tes, which hosts a full curriculum of maths lessons developed in collaboration with White Rose Maths, available free on its resources site

279 In the last month, as Christmas shopping gets under way and the weather gets colder, a designer boutique has sold four times as many scarves as sunglasses. In total, through combined sales of both, they have taken £2,835 so far. Sunglasses cost £90 more than scarves. The sale of scarves has raised £405 more than sunglasses.

How many pairs of sunglasses did the boutique sell?

Tes, which hosts a full curriculum of maths lessons developed in collaboration with White Rose Maths, available free on its resources site

280 In the song 'The 12 days of Christmas', how many presents does your true love give to you on the 12th day?

If the song carried on, how many presents would they give you on the 100th day?

Dr Kit Yates, Department for Mathematical Sciences at the University of Bath

281 You are at a New Year's Eve party with 50 guests. Before midnight everyone has to clink glasses with everyone else at the party so that the last clink falls on the stroke of midnight. To make sure no clinks are missed, clinking glasses has to be done one pair at a time. Each clink takes one second.

What time must the first clink occur?

Dr Kit Yates, Department for Mathematical Sciences at the University of Bath

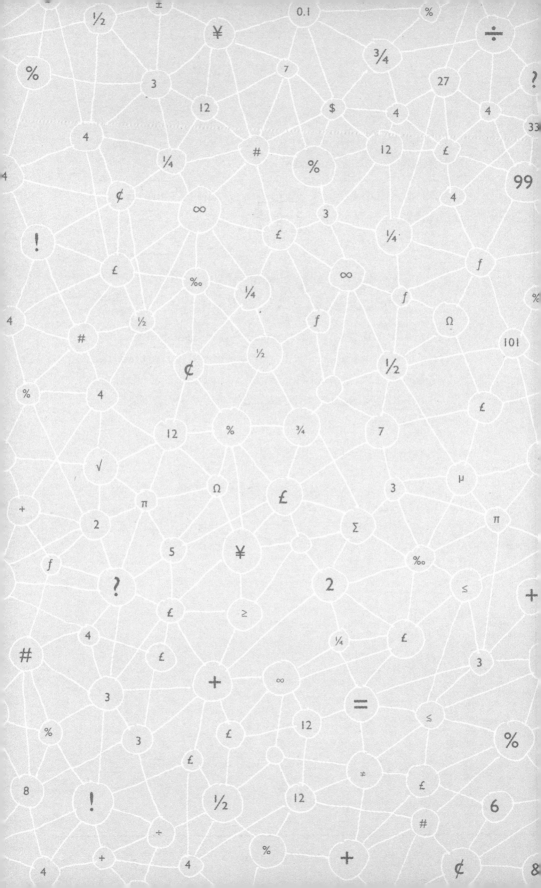

THE
ANSWERS

1 • Baker's dozen is 13, minus 5 gives the number   8

   • Nothing is the answer to the classic riddle   0

   • The number of planets in the solar system is   8

   • Hognut is an anagram of nought   0

   8-0-8-0...Ate nothing, ate nothing.

2 New Year's Eve, 1977.
   She will be 40 (FORTY).

3 • Eminem

   • Remainer

   • Romanian

   Ø ee

   Ø eae

   Ø oaa

   All that remains are vowels but, alas, there is no I and there is
   no U (You).

4   Julius Caesar. These are the sources for the names of every other month in the calendar. January is named for Janus, the two-faced god; March is named for Mars; May is named for the goddess Maia; July is named for Julius Caesar.

5   The number of shots is the sum of the Roman numerals in the words, for example, vodka has a 'V' and a 'D' which are 5 and 500 in Roman numerals, hence 505. So Metaxa becomes 1,010: M is 1,000 and X is 10.

6   Q belongs in the (IL) group. In the NATO phonetic alphabet, those letters would become different names of places (India, Lima and Quebec), where the other groups are Greek letters (Alpha, Delta), names (Charlie, Juliet and so on), and dances (Foxtrot, Tango).

7   R. They are the last letters of months of the year.

8   Most people think that when you step back from the bathroom mirror, you can see more of yourself, but this is not the case. As long as the mirror is vertical and the floor is horizontal, the amount of yourself that you can see doesn't change as you walk back, though you do of course appear smaller. As he steps back, Eric can still only see down to his navel, so the answer is (b).

9   The average number of sisters is the same for boys and girls. This comes as a surprise to most people.

We do need to assume here that the gender of the next child born is equivalent to the random toss of a coin, that is, it is not influenced by what happened previously. (This is very close to what happens in reality.)

In families that have a boy and a girl, the boy has a sister and the girl doesn't, and this leads most people to reckon that, on average, boys will have more sisters than girls. But this is forgetting all-boy and all-girl families, which cancel out the effect of mixed families. For example, two-child families will, with equal likelihood, be Boy-Boy, Boy-Girl, Girl-Boy or Girl-Girl. The four girls here have a total of two sisters, and so do the four boys – so there is an average of half a sister per child. Likewise, for families with more than two children, boys and girls turn out to have the same average number of sisters as each other.

An even more surprising result is that boys and girls have the same average number of sisters as each other, even if the population of boys and girls isn't split 50–50. For further discussion about this puzzle, see this blog: www.robeastaway.com/blog/sisters.

10   The bookmarks are less than 1cm apart. When you take a book off the shelf, the first page is on the right of the spine, not the left. So Aardvark is on the right of the first volume and Zebra is on the left of the second. The two are separated by the book covers and a few pages, so 4mm and a bit. To the nearest centimetre, this is going to be either 0cm or 1cm, but certainly not 9cm or more!

11   Behind the door was a WC. The room was a gents' toilet, and the door was to one of the cubicles. The letters were part of the VACANT ENGAGED indicator, which had been only partly slid across. (This is, by the way, a true story.)

12   The surprise is that all of the clues have the same nine-letter answer, PRESIDENT:

1.   pres-ID-ent

2.   P – Resident

3.   'president' is an anagram of 'tried pens'

13   Alice should take one orange. Then, whatever Bob takes next, Alice can ensure that, after her second turn, only two single (but different) pieces of fruit will remain, from which point her victory is guaranteed.

14   The answer is 98 – it is possible that every frog ends up in the top left square or the square to its right.

   To see why 99 empty squares is impossible, imagine colouring the grid like a chessboard. Every jump is either from black to white or from white to black. So after 100 jumps, every frog ends on the same colour square that they started with. Thus we cannot have every frog end up on a single square.

15   The cheapest book cost 90p (the other two books cost £2.70 and £7.20).

16   The list begins 20, 17, 3, 14, 11, 3, 8, 5, 3, 2, 1, 1, 0, 1, 1, 0, 1, 1, 0, 1, 1, 0...

   So there are ten numbers, followed by lots of repeated blocks of 1, 1, 0. This means that the 13th number is 0, and every third term after this is also 0. So the 16th, 19th, 22nd, 25th...2,011th, 2,014th and 2,017th terms will all be 0, thus the last number Dave writes is a 0.

17   George will eat 11 blueberries on the final day, having eaten 4, 5, 6, 7, 8, 9 and 10 on the other days.

18   Alice can guarantee two-thirds of the cake, by cutting the original cake in the ratio 2 to 1. If she makes any other cut, Bob can cut and choose strategically to prevent Alice taking two-thirds.

19   The answer is 32 chairs. You can approach this in different ways, but here is one explanation:

206 legs minus the 6 legs of the staff = 200 legs. On average, at each table, there are 3 table legs, 16 chair legs and 6 customer legs, which gives a total of 25 legs per table. 200 divided by 25 is 8, hence there are 8 tables. As there are 4 chairs at each table, the answer is therefore 32 chairs.

20   The minimum number of crossings is nine. You can approach this in different ways, but here is one explanation (we'll assume that the party is initially on the near bank and wishes to cross to the far bank):

If an adult crosses to the far bank, then there has to be a child waiting there to bring the raft back (unless an adult immediately brings the raft back – but this represents a wasted journey). This is possible only if the first two crossings involve both children crossing to the far bank and one of them staying there while the other brings the raft back.

The third crossing involves the first adult crossing to the far bank, and on the fourth crossing the child waiting on the far bank brings the raft back to the near bank. So after four crossings, one of the adults is on the far bank and the remainder of the party is on the near bank.

This procedure is repeated so that after eight crossings, both adults are on the far bank and both children are on the near bank. A ninth and final crossing then takes both children to the far bank.

21 The answer is that only Knave 4 is telling the truth. You can approach this in different ways, but here is one way of thinking about the puzzle:

The knaves all disagree, so at most one of them can be telling the truth.

If one of them is telling the truth, then four of them are lying, so four ate the tarts. Hence Knave 4 alone is telling the truth.

If all five knaves are lying, then all five ate the tarts. But then this makes Knave 5's statement true, which is a contradiction.

Therefore exactly one of the knaves (Knave 4) is telling the truth.

22 Every hour, one clock goes forwards by two hours and the other goes back by one hour, so the difference between them grows by three hours. Eventually, after eight hours, they will be 24 hours apart, or in other words, they show the same time again. Eight hours after 13:00 is 21:00, at which time the clocks will both be showing 05:00.

23   The only digits on the digital clock display that will appear the same when reflected in the glass tabletop are 0, 1, 3 and 8. So it is necessary to find the number of times in a 24-hour period that the display on the clock is made up only of these digits.

There are two possibilities for the first digit: 0 or 1.

There are four possibilities for the second digit: 0, 1, 3 or 8.

There are three possibilities for the third digit: 0, 1 or 3.

There are four possibilities for the fourth digit: 0, 1, 3 or 8.

To find the total number of possible times, we can multiply together the number of possibilities for each digit.

Therefore the number of times that the display and reflection will appear the same is

$2 \times 4 \times 3 \times 4 = 96$

24   October has 31 days so, in any year, in October there will be three days of the week that occur five times and four days that occur four times.

As there were exactly four Tuesdays and exactly four Fridays, there could not have been five Wednesdays or five Thursdays, so the days that occurred five times were Saturday, Sunday and Monday.

Therefore, 1 October must have been a Saturday, which means that 31 October was a Monday.

25 The finished quilt measures 32 inches by 33 inches (2 foot 8 inches). You can approach this in different ways, but here is one explanation:

The nine patchwork squares have areas of 1, 16, 49, 64, 81, 100, 196, 225 and 324 square inches, so the total area of the quilt is 1,056 square inches. Therefore, the length and width of the quilt have to multiply together to give 1,056. As both dimensions must be more than 18 (the side length of the biggest patchwork square), the possibilities are 22 inches by 48 inches, 24 inches by 44 inches or 32 inches by 33 inches. However, only the third of these possibilities can be completed without gaps and overlaps, as in the diagram below, which can also be rotated or reflected.

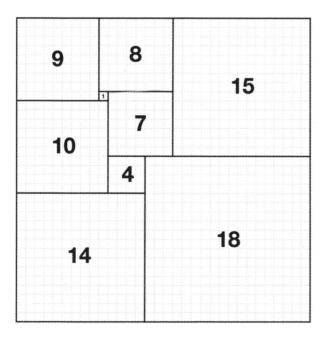

26 Yes. There are a few possible routes, but they must start or finish at Trafalgar, if we assume that the boat is not allowed to leave the Shipping Forecast areas. If the boat is allowed to travel outside the Shipping Forecast areas, then this restriction does not apply because Trafalgar can be reached by bypassing FitzRoy.

Here is one example route that remains entirely within the Shipping Forecast areas:

Trafalgar, FitzRoy, Biscay, Plymouth, Portland, Wight, Dover, Thames, Humber, German Bight, Dogger, Tyne, Forth, Cromarty, Forties, Fisher, South Utsire, North Utsire, Viking, Fair Isle, Faroes, Southeast Iceland, Bailey, Hebrides, Rockall, Malin, Irish Sea, Lundy, Fastnet, Sole, Shannon.

27 50 per cent. This problem is often stated in terms of passengers trying to board an aeroplane. Amazingly, the answer doesn't depend on the number of seats. We need simply observe that when the final passenger boards the train, the remaining seat will either be their reserved seat or the unassigned seat, with an equal probability of either choice.

28 Seven. This is a variation on the famous four-colour theorem, which states that on any map (a plane divided up into contiguous regions) no more than four colours are required to be able to colour the map so that no two regions of the same colour will share a boundary. An alternative way of stating the same result is that four is the maximum number of different colours that allow designs in which regions of every colour all touch each other on a plane, ignoring point contact. On a ring doughnut (or torus), the result is different and in fact you need seven colours: 'the seven-colour map theorem'.

29 73 and 37.

30 Surprisingly, only 27 weeks.

At week 1, you would be given 1p.

At week 2, you would be given 2p, making your total 3p.

At week 12, you would be given £20.48, making your total £30.72

At week 27, you would be given £671,088.64, making your total £1,006,632.96.

31   Nine blue balls and one other ball of a different colour.

Details of a possible solution:

Splitting the ten balls into two groups of five balls will give a 50 per cent chance that one of the two groups would contain five blue balls.

32   42 years old.

Details of a possible solution:

30 years is the age when you count five days in a week.

Hence, six years is the age when you count one day in a week.

So, 42 years is the age when you have seven days in a week.

33   Yes. Near the South Pole, there is a circle of latitude of circumference 5km. From any point on this circle, travel directly north 5km. This provides a starting point for the journey described in the puzzle. There are no bears near the South Pole. There are other solutions, though, which are left for the reader to discover.

34 7:21pm and 49 $\frac{1}{11}$ seconds.

The key idea in solving this problem is to express both the angle of the minute hand and the angle of the hour hand in terms of the number of minutes that have passed since noon. The hands will be perpendicular when the difference between these two quantities is ±90 degrees, plus a multiple of 360 degrees. At t minutes after noon, the minute hand is at angle $6t$ degrees and the hour hand is at angle $t/2$ degrees.

35 There are 16 hours between the first and last pill. There are three (not four!) intervals between each dose.

He should leave gaps of 16/3 = 5 hours 20 mins.

36 There are 120 arrangements. In constructing an arrangement of this six-letter word, we need only be concerned with the placement of the letters X, T and R. There are six possible choices for the position of X. For each choice of X, there are five remaining choices for the position of T, leaving four choices for the position of R. The total number of choices is thus $6 \times 5 \times 4 = 120$.

37 The year DCCCLXXXVIII, or 888 in decimal.

38 11.

Let T, A, W be the set of people surveyed who listen to *Today*, *The Archers* and *Woman's Hour* respectively. In the diagram below, the sizes of the sets are $|T| = 32$, $|A| = 26$, and $|W| = 30$. The total size of the surveyed set is 50. The sum $|T|+|A|+|W| = 32 + 26 + 30$ overestimates this quantity because it includes each doubly shaded region twice. Subtracting these gives a quantity $32 + 26 + 30 - 15 - 18 - 16$ that underestimates 50; the triply shaded region has been removed from our reckoning. Let X denote the set of people who listen to all three programmes. Then $50 = 32 + 26 + 30 - 15 - 18 - 16 + |X|$, from which one may deduce $|X| = 50 - 32 - 26 - 30 + 15 + 18 + 16 = 11$.

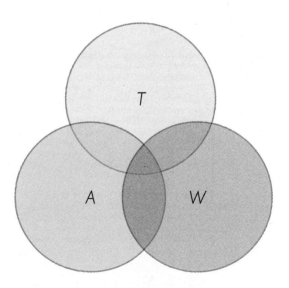

39   Great charter = Magna Carta = 1215.

Beastly number = 666.

The Election Bill was enacted as the House of Keys Election Act 1881 = 1215 + 666.

The Act gave the franchise to, among others, all spinsters and widows over 21 who owned real estate within the district of the annual value of not less than £4.

40   They have relatives who gave their names to Bond villains. (Richard Drax's grandfather Reginald inspired Hugo Drax in *Moonraker*... Henry Blofeld's father inspired Ernst Stavro Blofeld, who appears in three 007 novels...and Dave Scaramanga's grandfather George inspired Francisco Scaramanga in *The Man with the Golden Gun*.)

41   Rubber bands. Escobar needed them for his cash.

42   Muhammad Ali. The first line is, 'Float like a butterfly, sting like a bee.'

43   The poppies at the Tower of London.

44   By landing their helicopters on it. Noel Edmonds' downdraft ruined Elton John's flowers as he landed to take him to Wembley for Live Aid, while Nick Mason maintains the grooves he left in Clarkson's croquet lawn will help him hit the ball straight.

45   Barack Obama, after eight years in the Oval Office.

46   Q.

47   The Prime Minister's initials forming a number in Roman numerals. (The Prime Minister was David Cameron – D is 500, C is 100, making 600.)

48 22. The number of letters in 'Wolverhampton Wanderers', the longest name of any team in the top four English football divisions. The shortest name is 'Bury'. Other notable clubs include Swindon Town – the only team whose name shares no letters with the word 'mackerel'; Hull City – the only team whose name contains no letters you can colour in; and Millwall – the only team whose name written in capitals contains no curves.

49 Dead as a dodo. That's when the bird became extinct.

50 The artists responsible for the first songs on the respective 'Now That's What I Call Music...' albums. The series took its name from a poster in the office of someone at Virgin Records, who liked eggs for breakfast – it was a 1920s advert for Danish bacon, in which a pig listening to a hen laying an egg says, 'Now, that's what I call music.'

51 Wales. This is the meaning of the place name Llanfairpwllgwyngyllgogerychwyrndrobwllllantysiliogogogoch.

52   107. Treble 19 and a bull's-eye.

53   One of the statements is true (and that is one of the first two).

54   If we consider the different outcomes that could happen:

- Red sky and storm – one out of four of the days

- Clear sky and storm – one out of four of the days

- Clear sky and no storm – two out of four of the days

This means that the shepherd will be incorrect one out of four of the days (when it is a clear sky and no storm) and will be correct three out of four of the days (the other outcomes).

So he is correct 75 per cent of the time.

55   The words are connected by the colours of the rainbow:

red tape, orange squash, yellow pages, green beans, blue blood, indigo snake, violet wood.

56   A well-known scoring system is to give the fish a score based on the values of its letters on Scrabble tiles. So the bass is worth six points.

A not so well-known scoring system is to multiply the number of vowels in the day by the number of consonants in the fish. Using this scoring system, the bass on Thursday is worth six points.

57   The shape formed is a regular hexagon. Three faces of the cube meet at each corner so, as you lower the cube, the intersection starts off as a point and grows into a triangle. The size of the triangle continues to grow as you lower the cube until it reaches its largest possible size. This happens when the water passes through all corners connected to the submerged corner by an edge of the cube. Any further lowering truncates the corners of the triangle and produces a six-sided figure, with the surface of the water intersecting all six sides of the cube. As you continue to lower the cube, the longer sides of the six-sided figure decrease in length and shorter sides increase in length until they all become exactly the same length. This happens when the water intersects the midpoints of all edges not connected to the corner connected to the string or its diametrically opposed corner. The rotational and reflective symmetry of the cube tells us that all the sides and angles are equal.

58 Regardless of the choice of seating after lunch, we have two possible outcomes: either Peter sits with his pre-lunch partner or he does not.

The seating after lunch is random, so the probability that Peter sits with Alexandra after lunch is one in five. In the other four in five cases where Peter does not sit with Alexandra after lunch, she sits with one of three people, only one of which results in a pair being repeated. So the probability of a pair being repeated is $1/5 + (4/5)(1/3) = 7/15$.

Alternatively, you can list all possible pairings and check that there are exactly 15 pairs, seven of which have at least one of P with A, I with R, E with D.

59 45 unapologetically hate-filled letters.

60 54kg.

61 24.

62 $13/30$.

63   Many playing cards do not have top/bottom symmetry. For example, the five of spades has three spades pointing in one direction and two pointing in the opposite direction. Other cards that have more of the suit symbols pointing one way than the other include the eight of hearts and the six of clubs. By laying out eight cards of this type so that each has the majority of its suit symbols being 'up', it is easy to see which card has been rotated.

64   It might seem obvious that the A road will have more traffic per hour. But this is not so. The faster cars go, the further apart they need to be for safety purposes. In the Highway Code it is recommended that to allow for reaction times you should use the two-second rule so that you are always two seconds behind the car in front, regardless of the road that you are on. So from a fixed point a car passes every two seconds.

As there are 3,600 seconds in an hour, this means that if you obey the Highway Code, you will have at most 1,800 an hour, regardless of the type of road.

65   Surprisingly, it's the circumference by quite a long way. Standard Nonic pint glasses (the ones with the bulge near the top) are 15.2cm high and have a top diameter of 8.7cm, giving a circumference of 27.3cm.

66 However you break the chocolate, it will take 11 cuts to separate the 12 squares because at each stage you increase the number of pieces of chocolate (which may consist of more than one square) by one until they are all separated.

67 Let the position of the minute hand (expressed as a fraction of a whole turn) be x (so that $x = \frac{1}{2}$ at the half hour) and the position of the hour hand be y (so that $y = 0$ at 12 noon and $y = 1$ at midnight). As the hour increases, x starts at 0, then increases to 1 and then jumps back to 0 when you pass the hour. The hour hand travels at $\frac{1}{12}$ the speed of the minute hand. If n whole hours have passed since midday, then...

$y = (n + x)/12$ where $n = 0, 1, 2, 3, 4...$

If the hands are in the same position then $x = y$

Therefore, $x = (n + x/12)$ so $12x = n + x$, so $11x = n$

Therefore, $x = n/11$ $n = 0, 1, 2, 3, 4...10$ as a fraction of the whole turn.

As there are 60 minutes in the hour, this means that $\frac{1}{11}$ of a whole turn is $\frac{60}{11} = 5$ minutes 27.27 seconds.

So the hands are at the same time at:

- Noon
- 5 minutes 27.27 seconds past 1pm
- 10 minutes 54.54 seconds past 2pm
- 16 minutes 21.81 seconds past 3pm

And so on.

68 28 years. As there are four years between leap years and seven days in the week, the calendar is the same after 4 x 7 = 28 years.

69 Certain. An estimate of the maximum number of hairs on a human heads is 200,000. There are over eight million people living in London. They can't all have a different number of hairs on their head as there aren't enough options, so at least two must have the same number of hairs on their head. This is known as the pigeonhole principle.

70 Surprisingly, the answer is exactly one half. Because your friend has one more child than you do, they either have more girls or more boys, but not both. If they were to have both more boys and more girls, then they would have to have at least two children more than you. Assuming equal probabilities of having either a girl or a boy, the probability of them having more girls is the same as the probability of having more boys. Since these are the only two options, the probability of them having more girls is 50 per cent or one half.

71 Monroe. Otherwise the fact would have been three out of the first four presidents, making it seem more sensational.

72   There are two types of twins: identical and fraternal. Among the fraternal twins (assuming a 50–50 gender ratio), half will be of the same sex (GG BB) and half of different sexes (GB BG).

However, each pair of identical twins comprises individuals of the same sex. No matter how large a proportion identical twins make up, there will always be more twins of the same sex than twins of different sexes.

73   Yes, she is right, because if not, then a temperature and wind speed reading would be enough to pinpoint exactly where you are on Earth. In that case, I could make a map of the world by marking each place at the point whose x-coordinate is the temperature there and whose y-coordinate is the wind speed. It would be very distorted and stretched, but it would be a flat map of the world. But the world is not flat, so I can't do that!

So the Head of the Weather Department must have been right all along: at any time, there do have to be two places with the same wind speed and the same temperature.

74   a) Everton

b) Wolverhampton Wanderers

c) Tottenham Hotspur

75 The answer is 48 (there are eight ways to choose the pattern and then six ways to assign the colours).

76 The first letters of the authors' surnames spell out LOVE.

'The Owl and the Pussycat' is by Edward Lear. The Roman exiled to the Black Sea is Ovid (whose work includes the collection of poetry *Amores*). *Candide* is by Voltaire. *The Love Song of J Alfred Prufrock* by T S Eliot.

Lear, Ovid, Voltaire, Eliot.

77 340mph, and no bomber in 1943 could fly this fast. The speed of a falling object increases with time but only as the square root of height, as Newton and Galileo discovered. The trajectory of a falling bomb is therefore a parabola. To get the same angle of bounce at the water when dropped from twice the height means that it doesn't need to fly twice as fast, it only needs its speed increased by a factor of the square root of 2, about 1.41. So the planes would have to fly at 340mph.

78   You need to know that any number divided by four (there are four boxes) has a remainder of either 0, 1, 2 or 3. For example,

$87 = 84 + 3 = 4 \times 12 + 3$

so, it has remainder 3, while

$16 = 4 \times 4 + 0$

so, it has remainder 0 (or, in other words, it is divided perfectly by four.)

We split the 100 balls as follows:

First box: Remainder 0: 4, 8, 12...
Second box: Remainder 1: 1, 5, 9, 13...
Third box: Remainder 2: 2, 6, 10, 14...
Fourth box: Remainder 3: 3, 7, 11, 15...

And now, the real essence of the trick: suppose Justin picks, for example, one ball from each of the first, second and third boxes. Then, when we add them up, we get a number that leaves remainder 3. For example, say the balls are 12, 5, 6. Adding them up gives 23 which, when divided by 4, leaves remainder 3. Then, Mishal calculates the remainder of the number called out and if it's 3, her answer would be 'the fourth box'.

Similarly, if Justin picks:

(i) First, third and fourth boxes: the sum of his ball numbers will have remainder 1 and then she should say 'second box'.

(ii) First, second and fourth boxes: the sum of his ball numbers will have remainder 0 and then she should say 'third box'.

(iii) Second, third and fourth boxes: the sum of his ball numbers will have remainder 2 and then she should say 'first box'.

79 108. This is achieved with the six numbers 3, 9, 15, 21, 27 and 33.

80 The mother is aged 49 (which is 7 squared). Her three children are 2, 3, and 6. The squares of these are 4, 9 and 36 which sum up to 49.

81 Thanks to *Die Hard 3* for inspiring this puzzle! The five-pint jar is called Jar A and the three-pint jar is called Jar B.

1. Fill Jar A with five pints.

2. Pour three pints from Jar A into Jar B, so Jar A has two pints in it.

3. You pour away (or drink) the three pints in Jar B.

4. You pour the two pints from Jar A into Jar B.

5. Fill five pints into Jar A.

6. Pour one pint from Jar A into Jar B, so Jar A has four pints in it.

7. You pour away (or drink) the three pints in Jar B.

8. Pour three pints from Jar A into an empty Jar B.

9. You are left with one pint in Jar A. You have reached your final destination!

82 36. For nine people in total, the first person shakes hands with everyone else, that will total eight handshakes (since they do not shake hands with themselves).

The second person now shakes hands with everyone, except herself and the first person, with whom she has already shaken hands. This will add seven handshakes to the total.

Continuing along the line, each person will then add six, then five and so on until the ninth person, who will already have shaken hands with everyone else, and will add zero handshakes to the total.

The total number of handshakes is: $8 + 7 + 6 + 5 + 4 + 3 + 2 + 1 = 36$

83 These are all the official mascots of the most recent Commonwealth Games.

84 17 June 2345 (written 17/06/2345).

85 The leaders send a gift that begins with the same letter as their capital city. So Theresa May sends a lantern from London, Vladimir Putin sends a mirror from Moscow and Donald Trump sends a watch from Washington, D.C. and so on. The capital city of Canada is Ottawa so Mr Trudeau can send any gift beginning with the letter 'o' – perhaps an ornament or even an oyster!

86 Draw a straight line between the routes that both runners took. The elite athlete's training plan would have given the outline of a '2' figure and his training partner's route would give the outline of a '6'. Combine these together and you get 26, the number of miles in a marathon.

87 If you look at the acronym for each of the songs they spell out CHOIR (France), VOICE (Germany), SCALE (Spain), LYRIC (Italy) and AZERO (UK). The first four spell out words to do with music whereas the UK's just spells 'a zero', quite literally 'nul points'!

88   The capital cities of Paraguay, Thailand, Australia and the Republic
of Ireland respectively are Asunción, Bangkok, Canberra and Dublin.
So this follows an alphabetical list. There is no recognised capital of a
sovereign state with the letter E. But we can continue with 6 as F would
be Freetown of Sierra Leone.

89   Burkina Faso. The number represents the number of syllables per
word in the name of a country, so there may be other options with
five syllables.

90   London. The number represents the number of that summer Games as
an Olympiad (note that some numbered Olympiads were cancelled due
to war, such as 6 in 1916, 12 in 1940 and 13 in 1944 respectively).

91   Birmingham. These are the second largest cities in each country
by population.

92 The numbers represent the number of colours on a national flag. For a national flag with one colour, the Libyan flag was just a green field until 2011. The country has since re-adopted its flag from 1951 with four colours.

93 These are the countries that have hosted the Winter Olympic Games of that series. The first was held in France (Chamonix), the fourth in Germany (Garmisch-Partenkirchen), the ninth in Austria (Innsbruck) and the 16th in France (Albertville). The host country of the 25th Winter Olympics will be selected in Milan in September 2019.

94 Luxembourg. There are four European states where the capital city has the same name as the state.

In this pattern their names shift position to the right, by one, on each subsequent line from first word on the first line.

95 England is a good answer, and so is Switzerland, Poland, Indonesia and so on. These are countries that have the same colours on their flag as the football team has on their strip, so any country with a red and white flag is a valid answer.

96 35. You always work out the multiplication bit before the addition bit (unless there are brackets to tell you otherwise). So it's not 80, as people might think, if they did 5 + 3, then multiplied by 10. This might feel like a stupid rule, but it's important to get it right when communicating with numbers!

97 One in six, or $\frac{1}{6}$. For most people, intuition says that getting a six must be less likely when you've already rolled a bunch of sixes, but that isn't the case.

98 288cm.

Details of a possible solution:

Legs $(L) = 60 + \frac{3}{4}b$
Body $(b) = \frac{1}{3}(60 + b + L)$

The next stage to solve this challenge is to put these together:

$3b = 60 + b + (60 + \frac{3}{4}b)$
$3b = 120 + \frac{7}{4}b$
$\frac{5}{4}b = 120$
$b = 96$

Now we have the body (b) and the head, you can find the answer. The giant is $60 + 96 + 132 = 288$cm.

99   Three and three-sevenths minutes.

Details of a possible solution:

Speed = Distance/Time

Speed (v) with the wind (w) is $v + w = \frac{1}{3}$

Speed against the wind is $v - w = \frac{1}{4}$

By adding these you get $2v = \frac{1}{3} + \frac{1}{4}$, which gives $v = \frac{7}{24}$

Remember speed = distance divided by time; hence his time for the mile without wind would be $3\frac{3}{7}$ minutes.

100 One answer could be $231 + 231 = 462$

Using carry-overs to obtain $236 + 236 = 472$

All 16 answers are:

$206 + 206 = 412$, $216 + 216 = 432$, $231 + 231 = 462$, $236 + 236 = 472$, $271 + 271 = 542$, $281 + 281 = 562$, $286 + 286 = 572$, $291 + 291 = 582$, $407 + 407 = 814$, $417 + 417 = 834$, $427 + 427 = 854$, $432 + 432 = 864$, $452 + 452 = 904$, $457 + 457 = 914$, $467 + 467 = 934$, $482 + 482 = 964$.

101 Three for the price of two is a better deal. If you compare cocktails that normally cost £6 each, the first pub would charge you £12 for three cocktails, whereas the second pub would charge you £12.60 (the normal price of £18 × 0.7 for the 30 per cent off).

102 19p.

There are theoretical ways to solve this, but a more intuitive one is to think about making 20p and trying to make bigger sums from that starting point. You can make 20p with four 5p pieces, and then you can make 21p by changing one of the 5p pieces for a 6p. Then you can make 22p by changing another 5p for a 6p, and the same for making 23p and 24p. By the time you get to 25p, you can use all 5p pieces again (five this time). The same goes for making all the values up to 30p in the same way, and the same up to 35p, 40p and so on.

Now we know we can use 5p and 6p to make 20p and everything bigger, the next number to try is 19p. Using no 6p pieces won't work (you can't make 19p just with 5p coins), and using one 6p would need 13p in 5p pieces, which won't work. Using two 6p pieces would leave 7p to be made in 5p pieces, which also won't work, and using three 6p pieces would leave 1p left. Using four or more 6p coins would make an amount bigger than 19p.

So we've proved that 19p is impossible and that everything from 20p and above is possible, so 19p is the answer.

103 £10.43. For example: 4 × £2, 1 × £1, 1 × 50p, 4 × 20p, 1 × 5p, 4 × 2p.

104 17. The twins must be five years old and the boy seven years old.

105 Zero. As 2017 is odd it cannot be the sum of two odd prime numbers, so it could only be the sum of an even prime number and an odd prime number. But two is the only even prime number. So the only possibly sum is 2017 = 2 + 2015. However, this does not work as 2015 is not prime.

106 Four. Each face is adjacent to a ring of five other faces, each touching two other faces of this ring. Three different colours are needed for the colours of the faces in this ring, as their colours cannot just alternate between two colours. A fourth colour is then needed for the face they surround. So at least four colours are needed. It is easy to see that four colours are sufficient.

107 There are seven possible solutions. However you approached this, finding them, and convincing yourself that you've found all the solutions, gives a great opportunity for some systematic thinking and mathematical reasoning as you eliminate possibilities.

938 + 938 = 1876

928 + 928 = 1856

867 + 867 = 1734

846 + 846 = 1692

836 + 836 = 1672

765 + 765 = 1530

734 + 734 = 1468

108 Imagine 10,000 explorers. Of these, 99 per cent (which is 10,000 × 99/100 = 9,900) will die. What is the likelihood that Livingwood is in this unfortunate subset? On average, the soothsayer correctly predicts the deaths of 9,900 × 90/100 = 8,910 of these travellers. She is mistakenly optimistic about 9,900 - 8,910 = 990 of them. She correctly predicts that 100 × 192/200 = 96 of the lucky 100 will survive, but is unduly morbid about the prospects of the remaining 100 - 96 = 4 travellers. Of the 990 + 96 travellers who are predicted to survive, only 96 actually do.

Dr Livingwood's chance of survival is:

$$\frac{96}{990 + 96} \times 100 = 8.8\%.$$

He should be concerned.

109 There are at least 49 children. With this many children, it cannot be the case that each month has fewer than five birthdays, for then there would be $4 \times 12 = 48$ or fewer children. Conversely, were there 48 or fewer children in the class, then it would be possible for each month to have fewer than five birthdays.

110 42, the answer to the question about life, the universe and everything! There are clever ways to compute this so-called partition number without having to list all 42 possibilities. One idea is to classify the arrangements according to the largest table. There are ten such categories. Further investigation is left to the reader.

Partition numbers have been a topic of mathematical interest for over 300 years and were studied extensively by Srinivasa Ramanujan and Godfrey Harold Hardy in the early 20th century. Their collaboration inspired Simon McBurney's play *A Disappearing Number* and the 2015 film *The Man Who Knew Infinity*, starring Dev Patel and Jeremy Irons. Partition numbers appear in both these works.

111 200 bees. The bee population growth is related to the Fibonacci sequence.

112 120 interviews. If the order in which she tells the three jokes is significant, there are $10 \times 9 \times 8 = 720$ permutations of three jokes. Each set of jokes corresponds to exactly six permutations. Thus, there are $720/6 = 120$ distinct sets of jokes. If the condition 'repeat the same set of jokes twice' is interpreted to mean that she tells the same set of jokes on three occasions, the answer is $120 \times 2 = 240$ interviews.

113 2,241 candles.

- Burning the initial inventory gives 2,017 stubs, from which one may produce 201 new candles and 7 left-over stubs.

- After burning the new candles, there are $201 + 7 = 208$ stubs. These can be fashioned into 20 candles, with 8 stubs remaining.

- Burning these 20 candles, one will have $20 + 8 = 28$ stubs. The stubs may be reformed into two candles and eight stubs.

- Burning gives $2 + 8 = 10$ stubs, which can be turned into one final candle!

The total number of candles is $2,017 + 201 + 20 + 2 + 1 = 2,241$.

114 Six. Four people each shake hands with the other three, divided by two, because each shake features two people.

115 1 in 32. Each call has a 1 in 2 chance of being wrong, so the chances of all five being wrong are 1 in $(2 \times 2 \times 2 \times 2 \times 2)$.

116 285.

117 134.

118 19.

119 371. If there were 11 books, that would give the right numbers, but that's not enough. If we set 11 of the books aside, the rest can be stacked exactly in fives, eights or nines. The smallest number that divides exactly by 5, 8 and 9 is 360 (= $5 \times 8 \times 9$) so there must be 360+11 = 371 books: 731 = $2 \times 360 + 11$ would also work, but that's too many.

120 25 coffees at full price costs £50, but would include 25 stickers, which is enough for four free coffees (and one sticker left over), so you would pay for 21 coffees, costing £42.

121 It is not possible for me to have been born in 1661 because I am a human. Rotating the piece of paper by 180 degrees, you see '1961–1991'. As we were born on New Year's Day, this means that we were 30 years old for each day in 1991, and so my evil twin was 30 years old when they died.

122 Using only the 1p, 2p, 5p, 10p, 20p, 50p and £1 coins, the smallest collection that will work is (1, 2, 2, 5, 10, 20, 20, 50), which has size eight. If you allow the (uncommon but still legal tender) 25p coin, there are three other solutions also of size eight. The collection (1, 1, 2, 5, 10, 20, 25, 50) is such an example.

The solutions can be constructed via a process called backtracking.

123 4½ metres per hour.

124 5. Add the two previous numbers to get the following number.

125 MAYBE, ENTER, MYTH, AN and BE.

126 Mexico and Sweden.

IMPRESS
MEADOWS
EXCITED
LIZARDS
ICICLES
COMPANY

127 Boat and boast.

128 157.5 seconds.

129 1W on the second row in the fourth column.

130 Reaction and creation.

131 37. Each number is added to the previous number to get the following number.

132 $8 \times 11 + 7 = 9 \times 10 + 5$.

133 Penguin. The three letter words are PAN, END, NAP, GET, USE, ICE and NET.

134 18:30.

135 Counter.

136 'It is not fair to ask of others what you are not willing to do yourself.'

137 1 hour 5 minutes.

138 Ten. The alphabetical values of the first and last letters are added together to give the miles.

139 13 of each of 5p, 10p, 50p and £1.

140 74.

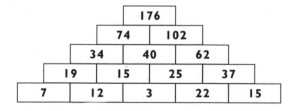

141 Improper, trooper, snooper, scalloper and blooper.

142 5. In each square the top left and bottom right numbers are multiplied to give the top right and bottom left.

143 6.37km. The spiral is a red herring. Just work it out from the total area. From C = 400m, you get that the ground has a radius of 63.7m. The area is then 12,732sq m and this must be the same as the distance travelled multiplied by the cut width, which is 2m. So the distance travelled is 6,366m.

144 Monkey, alpaca, donkey and wombat.

24	11	16	5	22
1	6	23	10	15
12	17		21	4
7	2	19	14	9
18	13	8	3	20

145 The second entry is eight billion (8,000,000,000). The second-last entry is two trillion two thousand two hundred and two (2,000,000,002,202).

This is an interesting list – a rare example of an infinite list where we know the first and last entries of that list.

146 A regular hexagon, √3 times bigger than the square. For a unit cube, the view down a body diagonal gives a hexagon ADBECF. The equilateral triangles ABC and DEF have sides of length √2 and the area of this triangle is √3/2. The total area of the hexagon is twice this by looking at the six triangles similar to ADB. Hence the total area of the shadow is √3.

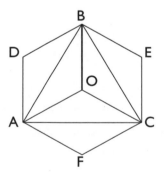

147 There may be multiple solutions but here is one. Number the cows 1, 2, 3, 4, 5, 6, 7, 8, 9, 10, 11, 12. Put them into three groups: A(1, 2, 3, 4), B(5, 6, 7, 8) and C(9, 10, 11, 12). Weigh group A and B. There are three possible outcomes:

Scenario 1: If they balance, then group C has the prized cow, so weigh 6, 7, 8 vs 9, 10, 11 with three possible outcomes:

1a) If 6, 7, 8 vs 9, 10, 11 balances, 12 is the prized cow. Weigh it against any other cow to determine if heavy or light.

1b) If 9, 10, 11 is heavy, then they contain a heavy cow. Weigh 9 vs 10; if balanced, then 11 is the odd heavy cow, else the heavier of 9 or 10 is the odd heavy cow.

1c) If 9, 10, 11 is light, then they contain a light cow. Weigh 9 vs 10; if balanced, then 11 is the odd light cow, else the lighter of 9 or 10 is the odd light cow.

Scenario 2: If group B > group A, then either 5, 6, 7, 8 contains a heavy cow or 1, 2, 3, 4 contains a light cow, so weigh 1, 2, 5 vs 3, 6, 12 with three possible outcomes:

2a) If 1, 2, 5 vs 3, 6, 12 balances, then either 4 is the odd light cow or 7 or 8 is the odd heavy cow. Weigh 7 vs 8; if they balance, then 4 is the odd light cow, or the heaviest of 7 vs 8 is the odd heavy cow.

2b) If 3, 6, 12 is heavy, then either 6 is the odd heavy cow or 1 or 2 is the odd light cow. Weigh 1 vs 2; if balanced, then 6 is the odd heavy cow, or the lightest of 1 vs 2 is the odd light cow.

2c) If 3, 6, 12 is light, then either 3 is light or 5 is heavy. Weigh 3 against any other cow; if balanced, then 5 is the odd heavy cow, else 3 is the odd light cow.

Scenario 3: If group A > group B, then either 1, 2, 3, 4 contains a heavy cow or 5, 6, 7, 8 contains a light cow, so weigh 5, 6, 1 vs 7, 2, 12 with three possible outcomes:

3a) If 5, 6, 1 vs 7, 2, 12 balances, then either 8 is the odd light cow or 3 or 4 is the odd heavy cow. Weigh 3 vs 4; if they balance, then 8 is the odd light cow, or the heaviest of 3 vs 4 is the odd heavy cow.

3b) If 7, 2, 12 is heavy, then either 2 is the odd heavy cow or 5 or 6 is the odd light cow. Weigh 5 vs 6; if balanced, then 2 is the odd heavy cow, or the lightest of 5 vs 6 is the odd light cow.

3c) If 7, 2, 12 is light, then either 7 is light or 1 is heavy. Weigh 7 against any other cow; if balanced, then 1 is the odd heavy cow, else 7 is the odd light cow.

148 No. All prime numbers (bigger than three) are divisible by 24. To prove this, use the 'Difference of Two Squares' result: $p^2 - 1 = (p - 1)(p + 1)$. If p is a prime number, then it must be odd. Any odd number squared is also odd, so $p - 1$ and $p + 1$ are adjacent even numbers, and one of these is divisible by four. In the case of $p = 7$, we have $p - 1 = 6$ and $p + 1 = 8$. Note that both are even, hence divisible by two, but one of these adjacent even numbers is also divisible by four. So the product $(p - 1)(p + 1)$ will be divisible by eight. Now note that p is not divisible by three because it is a prime. So one of $p - 1$ and $p + 1$ must be divisible by three because every third number is a multiple of three. In our case for $p = 7$, we see that $p - 1 = 6$ and this is divisible by three. So the product $(p - 1)(p + 1)$ is not only divisible by eight but also now by three. This proves then that $p^2 - 1 = (p - 1)(p + 1)$ is divisible by 24.

149 Martha wins.

The size and mass of the objects don't matter. You can work this out by equating potential and kinetic energy: mgh = $0.5mv^2 + 0.5J\omega^2$

For rolling without slip, note that $\omega = v/r$ and moment of inertia $J = mk^2r^2$ where k is the radius of gyration which depends only on the shape.

So the final speed $v = \sqrt{[2gh/(1 + k^2)]}$

The k^2 value for a solid ball, solid cylinder, hollow ball and hollow cylinder are 0.4, 0.5, $^2/_3$ and 1 respectively.

So the order of arrival is:

1. Billiard ball

2. Jar of Vegemite

3. Ping-pong ball

4. Empty can

150 $4 + 5 = 1 + 2 + 6 \ldots 9 = 9$

$16 + 25 = 1 + 4 + 36 \ldots 41 = 41$

151 The number is 34. You can approach this in different ways, but here is one way of thinking about the puzzle:

The number is less than 100, but five times the number is greater than 100, so it must be between 20 and 100.

Reversing the digits makes a prime number, so the first digit must be 1, 3, 7 or 9, as all two-digit prime numbers are odd and not divisible by 5. The number must be at least 20, so this rules out 1.

Since the digits add to a prime number, the possibilities are:

First Digit	Second Digit
3	0, 2, 4, 8
7	0, 4, 6
9	0, 2, 4, 8

The number must be one more than a multiple of 3. This leaves 34, 70, 76 and 94.

The number must have exactly one prime digit, which rules out 94.

The number must have exactly four factors, which rules out 70 and 76.

Therefore the number is 34.

152 The challenge for Utopia is to satisfy this equation:

The area of Utopia's pizza = five times the area of Italy's individual pizza's area.

Or:

$\pi ru^2 = 5\pi ri^2$ where ru and ri are respectively the radii of the Utopian and Italian pizzas.

Reducing the equation:

$$ru^2 = 5ri^2$$
$$\sqrt{(ru^2)} = \sqrt{(5ri^2)} \qquad \sqrt{} \text{ meaning the square root of a number}$$
$$ru = \sqrt{(5)}\,\sqrt{(ri^2)}$$
$$ru = \sqrt{(5)}ri$$

...and therein lies the problem. The square root of five is not a whole number by any stretch of the imagination: square root of one million places plus.

The resultant Utopian pizza radius will never be a whole number, thus 'violating' the Pizza Association of Naples (PAN) rules.

Even if the square root was taken to be 2.236067977, the pizza would need to have a radius of 5km to satisfy PAN. Of course, if there were only 4 continents:

$$\pi ru^2 = 4\pi\, i^2$$
$$ru^2 = 4ri^2$$
$$ru = 2ri$$

... which leads to a chit sheet that would be much more pleasant to a Utopian *pizzaiola* or *pizzaiolo*.

153 36. In mathematical terms, this question is asking about integers that can be represented in the form $5n + 7m$, for integer n and m. Combining 7s and 5s, we can eventually obtain all final digits 0 to 9, but final digit 3 doesn't occur until we have $(4 \times 7) + 5 = 33$. Thus it is not possible to represent 23 in the form $5n + 7m$ and so the required minimum capacity must be at least 24. If we want to ensure that there is definitely a mixture (that is, some red and some blue), then 24 is too small because 25, 28, 30 and 35 can only be made by buying entirely red or blue fish. Thus the minimum that ensures there can be a mixture of red and blue fish for all tanks of that size and those of greater integer capacity is 36.

154 3. This is an example of the so-called coin rotation paradox. The centre of the moving coin is a whole coin diameter away from the centre of the circular path, which means that the distance moved by the coin centre in a complete circuit of the fixed coin is twice the length of the coin's circumference ($2\pi d$ instead of $2\pi r$). Hence, in order to move its centre the required distance when viewed from above, the coin must rotate twice during its path. However, in terms of its contact with the edge of the fixed coin, each point of the perimeter touches only once on its path, so three steps are taken.

155 96. This type of problem is sometimes called an alphametic and there are a number of online solvers that will do the counting for you, but the basic solution method remains to count all valid possibilities.

156 64. We need a solution in positive integers of the equation $m^2 + g^2 = n^2$, where m^2 is Sam's mother's age, and g^2 is her grandmother's age. This equation has lots of solutions, but $m^2 = 36$ and $g^2 = 64$ give the only plausible ages for a mother and a grandmother.

157 One-fifth. Using algebra, it can be seen that this is the only solution.

158 8. She was left with 1/3 of the carrots, so she gave 2/3 away. As each child received 1/12 of the carrots, she has 2/3 ÷ 1/12 children.

2/3 ÷ 1/12 = 2/3 × 12/1 = 24/3 = 8.

159 43 – 27 = 16 cars remain.

Details of a possible solution:

$850(27) – 325(43) = 22{,}950 – 13{,}975 = 8{,}975$

Given $850X – 325Y = 8{,}975$

Solutions to this equation can be found as

$(X, Y) = (13t + 14, 34t + 9)$. As we are looking for $X, Y > 0$ and no more than 50 cars, the only solution is $t = 1$ for t as an integer.

160 His first spin lasts 1/33 minutes, his second is 1/22 minutes and his final spin is for 1/11 minutes. His total spinning time is $60 × (1/33 + 1/22 + 1/1) = 10$ seconds.

161 Quick answer:

Alice is 39 and Methuselah is 375.

Longer answer:

From the first clue, we know Alice's age is in the sequence

9; 15; 21; 27; 33; 39...

The second hint implies that her age is one of

11; 18; 25; 32; 39...

These sequences first coincide at age 39. This is the youngest possible age for Alice. From this information, we know Methuselah's age leaves remainder 39 on division by $6 \times 7 = 42$. It's therefore in the sequence

39; 81; 123...

The first number in this sequence that leaves remainder 1 on division by 11 is 375.

162 Yes, you can pay anything, because you can pay 1 plink by giving two 9s and getting a 17 in change. So if all else fails, you can just do that as often as you need to, though there will usually be less tedious ways.

The other question is harder. Divide the amount you owe by 9 and look at the remainder. Now pay 17 plinks and do the same again: the remainder has gone up by 1 (or has gone back to zero if it was 8). So by paying 17 plinks no more than eight times, you can get to a number that you can pay off in 9s. This works as long as you haven't already paid too much in 17s. So we can confidently say that we can manage any bill of at least 8 x 17 = 136 plink. In fact we can do slightly better than that: for example, $135 = 15 \times 9$, $134 = 17 + 13 \times 9$, $133 = 2 \times 17 + 11 \times 9$, $132 = 3 \times 17 + 9 \times 9$, and so on down to $128 = 7 \times 17 + 9$. Then it stops working, so the smallest bill we need change for is 127 plinks.

163 56 portions, enough for even the largest mathematical party! Let $P(n)$ be the maximum number of portions that can be obtained with n cuts. Make an additional cut that is not parallel to any of the other cuts, and that does not intersect any pair of existing cuts. The new cut has n points of intersection with the set of old cuts and produces $n + 1$ new portions. It's not possible to produce more than $n + 1$ new portions. That is, $P(n + 1) = n + 1 + P(n)$. With no cuts, there is one portion. Equally, $P(0) = 1$. An iterative application of the formula gives: $P(10) = 10 + 9 + 8 + ... + 2 + 1 + 1 = 56$.

164 Pipe A takes 4/3 hours to fill the tank so its rate of flow is 3/4 of a tank per hour. Pipe B takes 2 hours to fill the tank so its rate of flow is 1/2 of a tank per hour. If water is flowing in both pipes at the same time, the combined rate of flow is 3/4 + 1/2 = (3+2)/4 = 5/4 tanks per hour. Hence, using both pipes, the tank would be filled in 4/5 of an hour, or 48 minutes.

165 Surprisingly, the answer is always 1,089. For example 421 - 124 = 297; 297 + 792 = 1089 or 801 - 108 = 693; 693 + 396 = 1089.

166 Yes, she can. There are lots of possibilities. Here are some examples:

7, 37, 67, 97, 127

11, 41, 71, 101, 131

11, 71, 131, 191, 251

If the spacing isn't a multiple of 5, then one of her five chosen lily pads will be a multiple of 5. But 5 is the only multiple of 5 that's prime, and we're ruling that out. So the spacing Francesca chooses must be a multiple of 5. Similarly, she needs a spacing that's a multiple of 2 and of 3 (for the same sort of reason). So the spacing has to be a multiple of 30.

167 Each of these years can be written as a product of two different prime numbers:

1994 = 2 × 997

2005 = 5 × 401

2018 = 2 × 1009

The next year with this property is 2019 = 3 × 673.

168 Unexpectedly, the card is held in place even when one blows through the hole. This is because the air passing over the top of the card leads to a reduced pressure, which more than counteracts the pushing effect of the blowing. This behaviour, known as the Bernoulli effect, enables aircraft to fly.

169 No. The simplest way to see this is that each domino will cover one black and one white square; but the two corner squares that have been removed are both the same colour.

170 60 degrees. Suppose the angles are $a°$, $b°$ and $c°$, where $a > b > c$. Then and so $a - b = b - c$. Hence $a + c = 2c$. Since the sum of the angles of a triangle is 180 degrees, it follows that $3b = 180$ and hence $b = 60$.

171 1. Matchsticks are about 30cm long – hardly matchsticks!

2. Tent pole needs to be 193m long (some tent pole!)

For the first problem, use $C = 2\pi R$ for circumference C and radius R. Make the circumference bigger by x and the radius bigger by h then $C + x = 2\pi(R+h)$ so $x = 2\pi h$. With $x = 2m$ then $h = 1/\pi = 0.318$m.

The second problem involves trigonometry, but the really surprising result is worth the effort. See the diagram. Take Earth radius R. The rope is lifted up by height h. This means that the rope that is airborne contains the extra rope $x/2$ on each side plus the original length of rope that was on the ground $R\theta$. Using trigonometry on triangle OAB, $R\theta + x/2 = R\tan(\theta)$. It's useful to use the expansion $\tan(\theta) \sim \theta + \theta^3/3$ to give

$$x = 2R\theta^3/3. \qquad [1]$$

Now use trigonometry on OAB again, $(R + h)\cos(\theta) = R$ and note that h/R and θ are really small so use $\cos(\theta) \sim 1 - \theta^2/2$ which gives

$$h = R\theta^2/2. \qquad [2]$$

Eliminate θ from equations [1] and [2] to give

$$(2h/R)^3 = (3x/2R)^2$$ And with $R = 6{,}400$km $= 6.400.000$m for the Earth and $x = 2$m then $h = 193$m.

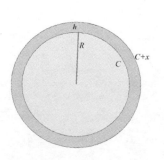

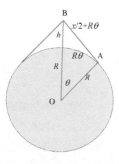

172 This conference allows representatives whose flags have an eagle on it. There is no sovereign Australasian country whose flag has an eagle on it.

American Samoa (with an eagle on its flag) in the South Pacific Ocean is part of a greater Australasian area. However it is not fully sovereign as it is an unincorporated territory of the United States and hence might be excluded from this unusual international conference!

173 24. These are the prime numbers but with one added to them. So 2, 3, 5, 7, 11, 13, 17, 19. The next prime number is 23. So the sequence continues with 24.

174 1,681,256. You combined the numerical powers of 2, 3 and 4. So the first number 2 to the power of 1, 3 to the power of 1, 4 to the power of 1, that is, 2, 3, 4 becomes 234. The second number is 2 to the power of 2, 3 to the power of 2 and 4 to the power of 2, that is, 4, 9, 16 becomes 4,916. And so on. So the fourth number is 2 to the power of 4, 3 to the power of 4 and 4 to the power of 4, that is, 16, 81, 256.

175 When the carts meet, they will have travelled for the same amount of time (say T), and since they were travelling in opposite directions, if we add the distances covered by both of them, we get 60km, the circumference of the circle. The distance covered by the red one is $30T$. The distance covered by the blue one is $20T$. Since the sum is 60, it follows that $60 = 20T + 30T = 50T$, so $T = 6/5$ hours. So the answer is that they meet after 1 hour and 12 minutes.

176 1704 (or 0417 for our American friends). These are dates when Easter Sunday falls in DDMM format, starting 1 April 2018, 21 April 2019, 12 April 2020, 4 April 2021 and then 17 April 2022.

177 These countries celebrate their independence days in those months and presumably there would be a good party for a student to celebrate! (Cambodia, 9 November 1953; Kenya, 12 December 1963; Australia, 26 January 1901; Saint Lucia, 22 February 1979; Greece, 25 March 1821; Republic of Ireland, 24 April 1916; and Cuba, 20 May 1902).

178 United Arab Emirates. If you write down the capital cities of these countries, they are Amman (Jordan), Algiers (Algeria), Addis Ababa (Ethiopia), Accra (Ghana) and Abuja (Nigeria). These capitals are listed in reverse alphabetical order for states that are fully independent and sovereign. Abu Dhabi from the UAE would be first in this list.

179 George Bush, Saddam Hussein and Tony Blair are linked through the abbreviation WMD (Weapons of Mass Destruction).

180 She was pregnant on each occasion. She acquired a passport for each of her children and dual citizenship for herself.

181 The letters are the initials of the numbers in the film titles:

2001: A Space Odyssey

300

Fahrenheit 451

1984

182 Astrology – the study of the movements and relative positions of celestial bodies – can almost be spelt by aligning star signs horizontally in an attempt to spell the word. However, the letter Y is missing from all star signs including Gemini, Aries, Libra and Cancer.

```
              A  q  u  a  r  i  u  s
        p  i  S  c  e  s
              T  a  u  r  u  s
        v  i  R  g  o
  c  a  p  r  i  c  O  r  n
              L  e  o
        s  c  O  r  p  i  o
        s  a  G  i  t  t  a  r  i  u  s
```

183 The 'time travel' is based on the operation of converting between decimal and octal numbers. For example, 25 December = 31 October, so the 'time traveller' celebrates Halloween on Christmas Day and Christmas Day at Halloween.

184 The minimum number with at least two pets is 5. This is achieved as follows: 5 people have all three animals, 1 person has just a rabbit, 10 people have just a cat, 7 people have just a dog, and one person has no pets at all.

185 Each multiple of 14 takes me back to the beginning, so after 28 stops I was back where I started. 37 is 9 more stops after that, so I was 4 stops past my home, and needed to wait another 10 stops.

186 The answer is 17/11/25, exactly 2,884 days after Christmas Day 2017. The date 7/5/21 is written 07/05/21 in the standard date format, which uses the digit 0.

187 The answer is approximately 7.6 per cent.

The answer depends on how you choose to define the words. The total number of letter combinations is straightforward to work out: it is 26 × 26 × 26 = 17,576. The number of valid three-letter words according to *Collins Scrabble Words* is 1,341. This gives a percentage of 100 × 1341/1756, approximately 7.6 per cent. In contrast, only 1.8 per cent of the possible two-letter combinations and 1.2 per cent of the four-letter combinations are words, again according to the *Collins Scrabble Words* lists.

188 They have 36 students (the reports are due in 9 days).

189 512.

> The tenth station is visited only once, so a photo must be taken then. For each of the other nine stations, the tourist has two possibilities: take a photo on the outward journey or the return journey. Hence the total number of possible orders for all ten photos is $2 \times 2 \times 2 \times 2 \times 2 \times 2 \times 2 \times 2 \times 2 = 512$.

190 The middle digit can be 0, 1, 2, 5 or 8. The first digit and last digit have to be 5, as 3 and 4 do not have rotational symmetry. The second digit can be 0, 1, 2, 5, 6, 8 or 9. So there are $5 \times 7 = 35$ possibilities. 59865 is the largest of these, so this is the 35th time it has happened since I got the car.

191 Fit three rows of postcards in portrait orientation, making seven columns. Then underneath, fit two rows in landscape orientation, making five columns, with a 1-inch gap.

Total: $3 \times 7 + 2 \times 5 = 31$ postcards.

192 If 50 people have 50 bicycles, there would only be 100 wheels. Every time we replace a bicycle with a tricycle we add a wheel. We need 117 wheels altogether, so 17 extra wheels. This means that 17 people brought a tricycle, and 33 people brought a bicycle.

193 5.

Doubling the length of each edge increases the volume of the tetrahedron by a factor of eight, so you might expect that eight of the smaller tetrahedrons will fit inside the larger. The catch is that, unlike cubes, tetrahedrons do not tessellate space. The best possible packing fraction, percentage of space that can be occupied, is still not known, but the record is 85.63 per cent. If this fraction could be achieved, then six small tetrahedrons would fit inside the larger. This last result is for unrestricted space, however, and once you add in the constraint that the tetrahedrons all have to fit completely inside the larger one, then the best that can be done is five.

194 The answer is, at most, 47. At first sight you might think that you need to test all 100 samples, but this is not the case because the samples can be pooled. The worst case is that the test is binary, indicating only whether the disease is present or not. We are interested in a methodology that has the minimum number of tests in the worst possible case, which is not the same as a method that has the lowest number of tests on average. This general type of problem is known as group testing and has been studied since the 1940s.

There is an information theoretic lower bound, which is the logarithm to base 2 of the number of possible states. In this case there are approximately 2,100,000,000,000 states (different ways in which up to nine numbers can be selected from 1 to 100), which gives a minimum bound of 41 tests. The question is whether this can ever be realised in practice. There is a method based on binary splitting (dividing small groups in two repeatedly) due to Hwang (1972), which can find the answer in, at most, 47 tests. Here's how it works:

We divide the 100 samples into 12 groups of eight samples each and one group of four. We test these groups (13 tests) and at most nine will test positive. We must now consider the separate possibilities:

• Exactly nine test positive, in which case we know that each group contains one diseased sample and we can find it in three tests per group using a binary search: test one half, if positive divide in half and repeat; if negative, divide the other group in half and repeat. This gives a total of $13 + 9 \times 3 = 40$ tests.

- Exactly eight test positive. Now we don't know whether each group contains one or two diseased samples. Proceed via binary search anyway, which will definitely yield eight diseased samples. We now have, at most, $8 \times 7 = 45$ untested samples with, at most, one diseased. This can be found in six more tests in another binary search. This gives a grand total of $13 + 8 \times 3 + 6 = 43$ tests.

- Exactly seven, six, five test positive. We use the same general approach to find a total of 47 tests, but because we now have more than one diseased sample after the first round of binary searches, we must repeat the overall process and subdivide the untested samples into groups of 16 (or eight or four or two) before binary searching.

- If four or fewer groups test positive, then we can simply test each sample in the group individually. The maximum number of these tests is 32 and then we have, at most, 45 tests in total.

Note that none of these methods requires any sample to be tested more than ten times.

Thus, this method guarantees an answer in, at most, 47 tests, but could there be an even better solution that gives an answer closer to the lower bound of 41?

195 It's the 50p, but the coins are of extremely similar volumes.

Looking up the geometric data from the Royal Mint reveals that a 2p coin has a diameter of 25.9mm and thickness of 2.03mm, whereas the 50p has a diameter of 27.3mm and thickness of 1.78mm (www.royalmint.com/discover/uk-coins/coin-design-and-specifications).

Ignoring the surface details on the coins, this information can be used to work out the desired volumes. The 2p coin is a cylinder, so the volume is π multiplied by the radius squared multiplied by the height, which gives approximately 1,070 cubic millimetres. The 50p coin is actually a Reuleaux heptagon (a non-circular shape of constant width) and careful geometry reveals that the face area of a 50p coin is approximately 0.7719 multiplied by the diameter squared. The volume follows on multiplication by the height and is 1,024 cubic millimetres. Based on these data, it would be the 2p coin that has the greater volume.

According to an e-mail from the Royal Mint, however, a 50p has a volume of 903.17 cubic millimetres and a 2p has a volume of 876.01 cubic millimetres. In other words, a 2p loses more volume to the surface patterns and it is, in fact, the 50p coin that has the greater volume.

196 No. In order to tie any kind of knot, a certain minimum length of cable is required. Establishing this minimum mathematically has been one focus of physical knot theory. Recent results in the theory have shown that the cable must be at least 15.66 times its diameter in order to tie the simplest form of knot: msp.org/gt/2006/10-1/p01.xhtml

197 Four. The chirp is started by a single cricket. Each other cricket either hears the chirp and emits its own (80 per cent chance) or doesn't hear the chirp (20 per cent chance). For an individual cricket, the probability that the chirping stops is given by $0.8P + 0.2$, where P is the probability that the chirping stops in response to the chirp of a single cricket. Assuming that the crickets behave independently then $P = (0.8P + 0.2)^{(N-1)}$, where N is the total number of crickets. There are only N – 1 repeats because one of the crickets made the first chirp!

If there is to be a less than 1 per cent chance that the chirping stops, then P must be less than 0.01. For $P = 0.01$, we have $0.01 = (0.008 + 0.2)^{(N-1)}$, which means that $N - 1 = \log 0.01/\log(0.208)$, which is approximately 2.93. This means that $N = 3.93$, and so a group of size four will ensure that the chirping continues.

198 The answer for two bricks of the same colour is 24, which can be found by thinking through the possibilities, and it is also a number that is easy to find online. The only subtlety is that one should avoid double-counting configurations that are the same when the bricks are rotated. If there are two bricks of different colours, then either one can be on the top, so this gives 48 different combinations.

The number of possibilities for increasing numbers of bricks gets very big, very quickly. See Søren Eilers' work: www.math.ku.dk/~eilers/lego.html.

199 If the trees are to be the same distance from each other, then they should be arranged in an equilateral triangle. The maximum possible equilateral triangle that fits in a square has one of its vertices in a corner and the others spaced along the two sides of the square that do not meet at the corner. A little thought shows that the angle between a side of the triangle and a side of the square meeting at the corner is 15 degrees, which means that you should plant the trees as close to the boundary as you can. The distance between the trees is approximately 1.035 times the length of the side of the field, so this is better than just planting at three of the corners.

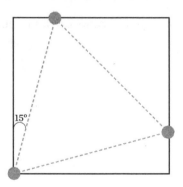

200 $2 \times 2 \times 2 \times 2 \times 2 \times 2 = 64$

There is one chance in 64 that you will take the correct path.

201 Anna has three, Charlotte has four and Bethany has nine.

This puzzle can be written as:

$C = 1 + A$

$B = 3A$

$B - 1 = 2C$

Therefore $B - 1 = 2(1 + A)$ giving $B = 3 + 2A$

Using this with $B = 3A$ gives $3A = 3 + 2A$ and hence $A = 3$

Substituting back for A into $C = 1 + A$ and $B = 3A$, we can find value of C and B.

202 The first player wins if he first takes two coins.

203 Rebecca, Harry and Juliet get eggs in the ratio of $2 : 3 : 4$

Dividing 54 by 9 $(2 + 3 + 4)$ gives 6.

Therefore Rebecca gets 12 (6×2) eggs, Harry 18 (6×3) eggs and Juliet 24 (6×4) eggs.

204 Onion. This puzzle takes its inspiration from the *Exeter Book*, a 10th-century codex of Old English poetry bequeathed to Exeter Cathedral by Leofric, first Bishop of Exeter. The book contains almost a hundred riddles on matters both sacred and profane.

205 Quick answer:

There are two possibilities: 1156 and 1225. One way to find a solution is to use the fact that $3^2 + 4^2 = 5^2$ to derive $(3 \times 7)^2 + (4 \times 7)^2 = (5 \times 7)^2$. That is, $441 + 784 = 1225$.

Longer answer:

The smallest four-digit square is $1024 = 32^2$. The largest three-digit square is $31^2 = 961$. So any solution is at most $961 + 961 = 1922 < 1936 = 44^2$. Any solution is therefore a four-digit square between 32^2 and 43^2. Moreover, at least one of the three-digit squares must be at least $1024/2 = 512 \approx (22.63)^2$. The problem is thus solved by finding three-digit squares x^2 of the form $z^2 - y^2$ where $32 \leq z \leq 43$, and $23 \leq y \leq 31$. A brute-force approach requires $12 \times 9 = 108$ computations and produces the solutions $34^2 = 16^2 + 30^2$ and $35^2 = 21^2 + 28^2$.

But there are more cunning approaches that significantly reduce the required computation. Here's one: note that $z^2 - y^2$ may be expressed as a product $(z + y) \times (z - y)$. The square x^2 must have the representation $x^2 = (z + y)(z - y) = ab$, where $a = z + y$ and $b = z - y$. The problem reduces to finding numbers 'a' and 'b' in an appropriate range such that the product is a square. The reader is left to determine an efficient procedure.

For interest, finding numbers whose product is a square is a crucial step in breaking popular secret codes such as the RSA cryptosystem.

206 Tabulate the sum:

1

1 + 2 +

1 + 2 + 3 +

1 + 2 + 3 + 4 +

...

1 + 2 + 3 + 4 + ... + 12

Adding up the columns, there are $12 \times 1 + 2 \times 11 + 3 \times 10 + ... + 1 \times 12 = 364$ gifts. One for each day of the (non-leap) year except Christmas!

207 Let u and v be the speeds of Mr and Mrs Claus respectively. From the result of the first race, we know that Mr Claus covers a distance of 80m in the same time that it takes Mrs Claus to run 100m. So, $v/u = 100/80 = 5/4$. Therefore, in the time it takes Mr Claus to run 100m, Mrs Claus runs $100 \times 5/4 = 125$m. Since Mrs Claus starts 20m behind the line, she will have run 120m before Mr Claus finishes the race. Mrs Claus still wins!

208 5cm. Make a cut vertically up from the start point and flatten the cylinder. The shortest route between the two points is a straight line. Pythagoras' Theorem gives the length of this line.

209 There are infinitely many primes, even though the fraction becomes tiny for larger numbers. The simplest way to see that there is no largest prime number is to assume that this is the case and then show that this leads to a contradiction. If you multiply all the prime numbers, from 2 up to the hypothetical largest prime, and then add 1 to this product you'll have found a number that is not divisible by any of this list of primes. But that means that it must be a prime number itself; as it is clearly larger than the hypothetical largest prime that hypothesis is contradicted. So there must be infinitely many primes. (Not that large primes are easy to find: there was a big press release in late 2017 when researchers found $2^{77,232,917} - 1$, a number with 23,249,425 digits, was shown to be a prime.)

210 The intuitive, but incorrect, answer is to reinforce those parts of the plane where the bullets are located. This is, in fact, what the Americans concluded and set about reinforcing these parts, until statistician Abraham Wald came along and said that instead it should be precisely those areas without bullet holes, namely the cockpit and the engines, that should be reinforced. There is no reason to suspect that bullet holes shouldn't be spread randomly throughout the whole plane, so where are the planes with bullet holes in the engine and the cockpit? Well, these planes never made it back, they were shot down and never returned from their mission. Those planes with bullet holes in the fuselage and wings are the planes that could survive hits and still make it back, so these areas of the plane are areas where you could afford to take hits. This is an example of selection bias.

211 1/500, or in general, for *N* seats the probability yours is left is 1 in *N*; the most intuitive explanation being that this story is equivalent to Jeremy boarding the train and picking his own seat at random, whereas if he has 500 seats to choose from, he has a 1/500 chance of choosing his own seat.

212 Let S = 3.6342342342.... Then $10S$ = 36.342342342... and $10000S$ = 36342.342342342...

Now $10000S - 10S = 9990S = 36342 - 36 = 36306$.

So $S = 36306/9990$.

To find the smallest pair, simplify the fraction by cancelling any prime factor that you find present on the top and the bottom. When you reach 2017/555, factorise 555 as $3 \times 5 \times 37$ and note that none of these numbers divides 2017 so the smallest pair of numbers is 2017 and 555.

213 The spots are 9in across. Volume scales as the cube of linear dimensions. So, if at the beginning we call the volume of the smaller balloon one unit, then the volume of the larger balloon is $12 \times 12 \times 12 = 1,728$ units, since the spots are 12 times as wide. That is a total volume of 1,729 units. After the exchange of air, the larger balloon has $10 \times 10 \times 10 = 1,000$ units volume, leaving 729 for the (still just) smaller balloon. Since $729 = 9 \times 9 \times 9$, this implies that the spots on the smaller balloon are now 9in across (perhaps surprisingly large).

Writing in 1940, Cambridge professor G H Hardy recounted of the Indian mathematical prodigy Srinivasa Ramanujan: 'I remember once going to see him when he was ill at Putney. I had ridden in taxi cab number 1729 and remarked that the number seemed to me rather a dull one, and that I hoped it was not an unfavourable omen. "No," he replied, "it is a very interesting number; it is the smallest number expressible as the sum of two cubes in two different ways."' ($1,729 = 12 \times 12 \times 12 + 1 \times 1 \times 1 = 10 \times 10 \times 10 + 9 \times 9 \times 9$)

The Unitarian chapel in Fulwood, Sheffield, has the date 1729 above the door. One of our colleagues likes to attend for that reason.

214 The longest segment in an equilateral triangle is one of the sides. So a smaller triangle will cover at most one vertex. This means that it is not possible to cover all three vertices of the larger triangle using only two smaller triangles.

215 The five words are connected by the five oceans: Arctic Monkeys, Atlantic City, Pacific Northwest, Indian Summer and Southern Comfort. So, the answer is 'The Ocean's Trilogy' (of films).

216 Mayonnaise contains the name of an Irish county whereas the others are each contained in the name of an Irish county.

217 A possible solution is to weigh HEAD against GLIB, BLED against JACK, and CALF against HIKE. Each weighing gives one of three possible outcomes: right heavy, left heavy or balanced. So there are 27 possible combinations. Three of these will never occur, and the other 24 correspond to the 24 different scenarios, as can be easily checked.

218 You can do this by arranging the six matches to form a three-dimensional pyramid with a triangular base and three triangular sides rising from the base. This object is called a regular tetrahedron, and is one of five Platonic solids considered by the ancient Greeks.

219 Knees, eyes, breakfast, years, mouth, share and ear are connected by animals; the bees knees, cat's eyes, a dog's breakfast, donkey's years, straight from the horse's mouth, the lion's share, a pig's ear.

220 The ninth block was E, and the sequence corresponded to the digits of pi (π). Replacing the letters with the numbers corresponding to their position in the alphabet gives the sequence 31415926. This sequence corresponds to the digits of π to seven decimal places. So, the next digit in the sequence is 5, which corresponds to the letter E.

221 1 in 5.

The chances of the children all picking different boxes is:

249/250 × 248/250 × 247/250 × 247/250 × 246/250 × 245/250 × 244/250 × 243/250 × 242/250 × 241/250 × 240/250

For the second child, 249 out of 250 boxes still have an egg inside. For the third child, 248 out of 250 boxes still have an egg inside – and so on until the 11th child where 240 out of 250 boxes still have an egg inside.

Multiplying all these together comes to 0.80, that is, 80 per cent or 4 in 5 chance of all the children picking different boxes. So the chance of at least one child finding an empty box is 1 – 0.80, that is, 20 per cent or 1 in 5.

222 41 and 83. The first number in each pair is prime. The second number is twice the first number plus one, and is also prime. The first primes in each pair are called Sophie Germain primes, after the French 19th-century mathematician who investigated them. The next-smallest Sophie Germain prime is 41 and its pair is 83. We still don't know whether there are infinitely many of them or not.

223 If the third assistant gets the X, it will look all right anyway. If he gets A or M or Y back to front, E upside down, or S both upside down and back to front, that will be all right too: so in those cases there is an even chance it won't matter. If he gets an R, there is only a one in four chance it won't matter: he has to get it right.

Then you just have to count cases. There are 84 possible sets of three letters that the third assistant could get, and three kinds of letter: X, R and others. One of those is XRR, and then his chances of putting up the right thing are 1/16; six more are RR and other (chances are 1/32); 12 are X, an R and other (1/8); 30 are R and two others, not X (1/16); 15 are X and two others, not R (1/4); 20 are three others, no X or R (1/8).

So the chances of it coming out right are $(1/16 + 6/32 + 12/8 + 30/16 + 15/4 + 20/8)/84 = (316/32)/84 = 79/(16 \times 84) = 79/1344$, which is 0.05877... or just about one in 17.

224 Although the challenger is just as good as the champion, the challenger's chances of becoming champion are only just better than three out of eight: actually 386/1024. (Three-eighths is 384/1024.)

There are two possible results for each game, not counting draws, which are rare in Mornington Crescent anyway: so there are 2 to the power of 10 (i.e. 1024) possible sequences of results in the first ten non-drawn games. Of those, 252 give a 5-5 scoreline (252 is the number of ways to choose 5 things out of 10), and in those cases the champion remains champion. In half of the other 772 cases, the champion wins anyway, 6-4 or better. Only in the other half, that's 386 cases, does the challenger become champion: so the challenger's chances are 386/1024.

The champion is really Bobby Fischer and the challenger is Anatoly Karpov. These were Fischer's proposed rules for his (chess, not Mornington Crescent) 1975 World Championship defence. Karpov, naturally, objected; Fischer refused to play under any other rules, and forfeited his title.

225 (a) 20% (b) 20% (c) 80%.

226 $5(2x + 8) - 24 = 10x + 16$

If John says his answer is 56, then we need to solve $10x + 16 = 56$

Therefore $10x = 40$ and the number John first started with was 4.

227 There are 252 ways. There are several ways to group the mince pies, and then we should count the number of ways of assigning them to presenters.

- One possibility is that one presenter has all five mince pies. There are six presenters, so there are six possibilities here.

- Or one person gets four and another one. There are six possibilities for the presenter who gets four pies, then for each of those there are five possibilities for the presenter who gets the remaining one. So there are 6 × 5 = 30 possibilities here.

- Or we could have three, two. This gives another 6 × 5 = 30 possibilities.

- Or we could group the pies as three, one and one. There are six possibilities for the presenter who gets three pies. Then five possibilities for a presenter who gets one pie and then four possibilities for a presenter who gets the remaining pie. But here we've counted each possibility twice (the assignment that gives Sarah three, Mishal one and Nick one is the same as the assignment that gives Sarah three, Nick one and Mishal one). So in total there are (6 × 5 × 4)/2 = 60 possibilities.

Keeping going in this way, here's a summary of the cases:

- Pies grouped as two, two, one: get 60 possibilities.

- Pies grouped as two, one, one, one: get 60 possibilities.

- Pies grouped as one, one, one, one, one: here we just need to choose the unlucky presenter who doesn't get a mince pie, so there are six possibilities.

Adding all of these possibilities, we see that there are 6 + 30 + 30 + 60 + 60 + 60 + 6 = 252 possibilities.

228 16. For this type of problem, known as the art gallery problem, if there are n sides, then the integer part of $n/3$ cameras will always suffice. In this case, the answer is the integer part of 50/3, which is 16.

229 John is 21. The numbers represent how many points the surnames of the *Today* programme presenters (such as Humphrys) would gain in a game of Scrabble. This would only include the raw points total per letter, however, and exclude any bonus points, such as for using up all your tiles.

230 Given that x is the 'numerical value of the card' and y is the 'suit value': $5(2x + 3) + y = 10x + 15 + y$. Hence, if the magician subtracts 15 from the total James says, the tens value is the numerical value of the card and the units value the suit. In this case, $79 - 15 = 64 = 6 \times 10 + 4$ so the card is the six of spades.

231 $9(x + 7) + 13 = 9x + 76 = 9(x + 8) + 4$, giving a multiple of nine plus four.

Using Digital roots theory (en.wikipedia.org/wiki/Digital_root) when adding digits of multiples of nine (9, 18, 27, 36, 45...), the answer is always nine. Hence the answer is four in this puzzle, regardless of which number Sarah initially selected.

232 Say Nick chooses a three-digit number (by the way, this puzzle works for any number, not just three-digit numbers), in general a three-digit number can be written in the form $100a + 10b + c$. Then scrambled, this could give $100b + 10c + a$. Subtracting these two numbers:

$(100a + 10b + c) - (100b + 10c + a) = 9(11a - 10b - c)$ giving a multiple of nine.

Using Digital roots theory (en.wikipedia.org/wiki/Digital_root) when adding digits of multiples of 9 (9, 18, 27, 36, 45...) the answer is always nine. Hence in this puzzle the answer is always nine if the circled number is included. This is regardless of which number Nick initially selects. In this particular case when Nick says '16' (sum of digits $1 + 6 = 7$) the magician knows that the circled number is two, as this makes the total nine ($7 + 2$).

233 The next character in the sequence is 'S'. The Roman numeral for '5' is 'V', '500' is 'D' and '1' is 'I'. Making the substitution into the above sequence gives: E, V, A, N, D, A, V, I, _, which makes us think of Evan Davis, the *Today* programme presenter 2008–2014.

234 The next two square years are $45 \times 45 = 2025$ and $46 \times 46 = 2116$. So, Justin will turn a square year in 2025. The square years before retirement age are 1, 4, 9, 16, 25, 36, 49, 64. So Justin turns 64 in 2025. This means that he was born in 1961.

235 Short answer:

The area of each pizza is proportional to the square of its circumference. Since 61 squared – 60 squared = (61 – 60)(61 + 60) = 121 = 11 squared, the answer is 11. Well done, John!

Detailed answer:

Remembering the formula for the circumference of a circle, we know that the radius of Sarah's pizza, which we denote by x, satisfies $2\pi x = 61$cm and the radius of John's pizza, which we denote by y, satisfies $2\pi y = 60$cm.

So the area of Sarah's pizza is $\pi x^2 = \pi(61/(2\pi))^2$ cm^2

and the area of John's pizza is $\pi y^2 = \pi(60/(2\pi))^2$ cm^2

The area of John's second pizza must equal the area of Sarah's pizza minus the area of John's first pizza. This means that the area of John's second pizza with radius z must satisfy $\pi z^2 = \pi(61/(2\pi))^2 - \pi(60/(2\pi))^2$.

This means that $z = 11/(2\pi)$ cm, which makes the circumference of John's second pizza equal to $2\pi z$cm $= 2\pi(11/(2\pi))$cm $= 11$cm.

Well done, John!

236 By the ninth day, Martha will have read more pages.

Martha's total after eight days $(1 + 2 + 4 + 8 + 16 + 32 + 64 + 128)$ is 255.

Nick's total after eight days $(10 + 20 + 30 + 40 + 50 + 60 + 70 + 80)$ is 360.

On the ninth day, Martha reads another 256 pages, taking her total up to 511 pages. Justin reads another 90 pages, taking his total up to 450 pages.

237 Divide the 25 × 36cm rectangle into a grid. Cut along the bold line. The sections can be rearranged to make a square.

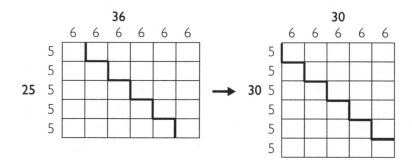

238 9:59:59 and 10:00:01

239 11911 and 434.

240 J J A S O N D J F M A M is a sequence of letters more familiar as the initials of the names of the month: June July August September October November December January February March April May.

241 Justin.

242 511. It is a knockout tournament and, logically, only the winner will remain undefeated. Every other competitor will lose one, and only one, match. So if there are four entrants, there will have be three matches, and three people have to lose. With eight entrants, there will be seven matches and seven people have to lose. With 128 entrants, there have to be 127 losers, and hence 127 matches. And for 512 participants (as it fits within the model of 2 to the power of n, that is, 2 to the power of 9), you will have 511 losers, so 511 matches.

243 The colours of the Tube lines in this journey are Red, Orange, Yellow, Green, Blue. If we take the first letters of these colours, this follows the start of the mnemonic 'Richard of York Gave Battle (In Vain)' to help remember the colours of the rainbow. Richard of York Gave Battle in Vain is said to refer to the defeat and death of Richard, Duke of York at the Battle of Wakefield in 1460 during the Wars of the Roses. As there are no Tube lines with the colours indigo or violet, this mnemonic would be incomplete and hence a history (or science) teacher would feel frustrated in not being able to complete a theoretical tube journey with these mnemonics colours!

244 Each time refers to the official hosting of a FIFA World Cup. It 'happens' when the host nation wins the World Cup. 1 = Uruguay in 1930; 2 = Italy in 1934l; 8 = England in 1966; 10 = West Germany in 1974; 11 = Argentina in 1978; 16 = France in 1998. Russia did not win their host World Cup in the 21st edition of the 2018 tournament.

245 4. It is the number of letters in each word in the opening sentence of Jane Austen's *Pride and Prejudice*. 'It is a truth universally acknowledged, that a single man in possession of a good fortune, must be in want of a wife.' The final word 'wife' has four characters.

246 We are talking about pets from the children's TV show *Blue Peter* (Petra the dog was the first pet, Jason was the first cat, Shelley was a tortoise, Iggy is a recent guide dog from the show). The answers to the four parts are Petra (city with Indiana Jones's holy grail), Jason (leader of the Argonauts), Mary Shelley (author of *The Modern Prometheus*) and Iggy Pop (the godfather of punk with a song called 'Lust for Life').

('Here's a problem we made earlier' alludes to the famous *Blue Peter* phrase, 'Here's one we made earlier.')

247 If there were five assassins, then even if Sherlock was lucky enough for a long time not to meet one of the assassins, the crazy gang would eliminate themselves two at a time until one lone assassin was left. That assassin could not be eliminated and would eventually bump into Sherlock and the great detective would perish; so Sherlock was right to refuse Moriarty's 'kind' offer, as he'd have no chance of survival at all if he did.

The second part sounds complicated, but it can be done in your head. I set a learned professor (no names, no pack drill) this question once. After ten minutes of scrawly algebra, he eventually reached the right answer. But we are a) lazy, b) intelligent and c) have no paper, so let's do it in our heads instead.

If Sherlock is to survive, he must be the last one standing. His survival means he never met an assassin. Now let's pretend he IS an assassin. Then we have a far easier puzzle in which seven assassins are in the maze. They eliminate each other pairwise until one is left – the one who never met another assassin. Obviously – by symmetry – each has an equal one in seven chance of being the last one standing, that is, of not having met another assassin. Since Sherlock's being an assassin or not being an assassin only counts for anything if he meets someone and if he survives or if he didn't meet anyone, one in seven must also be Sherlock's chances of survival.

248 100. If you multiply all the numbers by 100, you get the distances of races in increasing length at a standard men's Olympic track athletics programme. 100m, 200m, 400m, 800m, 1,500m, 5,000m and 10,000m. *Citius, altius, fortius* is the Olympic motto in Latin, which in English means 'Faster, higher, stronger'.

249 These are US Presidents who were popularly known by their middle names or nicknames. Hiram Ulysses Grant went by Ulysses (1869–77), Stephen Grover Cleveland went by Grover (1885–89, 1893–97), Thomas Woodrow Wilson went by Woodrow (1913–21), John Calvin Coolidge Jr. went by Calvin (1923–29), James Earl Carter, Jr. went by Jimmy (1977–81) and William Jefferson Clinton went by Bill (1993–2001).

250 If you take the first initial of each letter, you get I V X L C D M and this is a useful mnemonic for the value of Roman numerals in ascending order (1, 5, 10, 50, 100, 500, 1,000). And you might see lots of Roman numerals in Rome!

251 1,089.

252 21 March (the spring equinox), since his home must be on the North Pole, where the sun rises once a year.

253 A partridge in a pear tree is worth two reindeer. A pair of turtle doves is worth three reindeer. You can use trial and improvement or, if you remember GCSE maths, set up simultaneous equations to solve them!

254 6.

255 Chile or any other country that has its capital city starting with an 'S', as in Santiago for Chile. The capital cities of the countries in these lists are Sofia, Amman, Nassau, Tokyo and Athens; Copenhagen, Lima, Ankara and Ulaanbaatar. The first letters of these cities spell out SANTA CLAU. We need 'S' to finish 'Santa Claus'.

256 Anything where the Scrabble points value of the letters is 14. The gifts are equivalent to the Scrabble points value of their first name. Mishal and calendar are 11 points, Justin and clock are 13 points, Sarah and shoes are 8 points, Nick and scarf are 10 points.

257 90. There are ten people/reindeer in total, and each person has to buy nine presents (for everyone else except themselves), so that's $9 \times 10 = 90$ presents total.

258 45. If there were only two people, you'd need one cracker. If you add a third person, they'll need one cracker for each of the two other people, so 1 + 2 = 3 in total. If you add a fourth person, you'll need another three crackers so they can pull one with each of the first three, so 1 + 2 + 3 = 6 in total. So if there are ten people, it's 1 + 2 + 3 + 4 + 5 + 6 + 7 + 8 + 9 = 45.

It's not a coincidence that that's half the number of presents that would be exchanged (*see* Puzzle 257). For every cracker that gets pulled, each person pulling it needs to buy the other a present – so there are exactly twice as many presents as crackers.

259 135cm. 50 per cent deeper today is another 20cm, so 60cm in total tomorrow. 50 per cent deeper than that is another 30cm, so 90cm total in 2 days. 50 per cent deeper than that is another 45cm, so 135cm in total.

260 3/16. There are eight people that could be in charge of Scrooge's present – one of them will get something worth more than his lump of coal (Mrs Cratchit), and the other one will do so half of the time (Bob). So there's a 1.5/8 = 3/16 probability of Scrooge getting out more than he puts in.

261 15. There are two ways to split the cheeseboards (two and one, or one and two), three ways to split the puddings (three and one, two and two, or one and three) and five ways to split the boxes of chocolate (five and one, four and two, three and three, two and four, or one and five).

This gives us $2 \times 3 \times 5 = 30$ ways to split the items between the hampers. But only in half of them will the number of items in the large hamper be more than in the small hamper. So the final puzzle answer is $30/2 = 15$.

262 $9228 + 9228 = 18456$

263 Square numbered lights are switched on 1, 4, 9, 16, 25, 36.

This is because square numbers have an odd number of factors (for example, for four: 1, 2, 4) and all other numbers have an even number of factors (for example, for six: 1, 2, 3, 6).

264 Yes, you can time 45 minutes. Place your two candles in a way so that two of their wicks are touching. Now use two matches to light both ends of a candle of your choice. This means that one of the candles is lit at both ends and the other at one end. The candle lit at both ends will burn out in exactly 30 minutes. When this happens, the candle with only one lit wick has exactly 30 minutes left to burn out. So, if you light the only unlit wick at exactly the moment the candle with two burning wicks burns out, the second candle will burn out in exactly another 15 minutes. So, lighting the candles in this way will mean that the second candle will have burnt out after exactly 45 minutes.

265 There are three boys and three girls in the family. Each child gets one of the two sweets for £1 (i.e. six sweets for £3) and two of the three sweets for £1 (i.e. 12 for £4).

266 The lengths are $100 = 2 \times 2 \times 5 \times 5$ minutes, and $170 = 2 \times 5 \times 17$ minutes. The least common multiple is $2 \times 2 \times 5 \times 5 \times 17 = 1,700$ minutes, which is 28 hours, 20 minutes, taking them to 2.20pm on Christmas Day, in good time for the Queen's speech at 3pm.

267 There is no missing £30. The answer is in the way the puzzle is worded.

The new total for the bill is £560, which is £28 × 20 = £560.

Then you take away £10, which the waiter did not return, to get £550 now in the restaurant's possession. In reality, the £600 in the puzzle wording is irrelevant to how much the party ended up paying for the meal.

268 128.

269 Write A = Donner, B = Vixen, C = Comet, D = Blitzen. We must arrange the reindeer in the following pattern:

```
• •
• •
• •
• •
```

First note that for any given choice of positions for A, B, C and D, there is a total of 24 possible positions for the remaining reindeer (call them E, F, G and H), as 24 = 4 × 3 × 2 × 1.

By symmetry, we may suppose that A is either in the top-left position or the position directly below that. Every legal configuration can be derived from one of these restricted configurations by a reflection (or two) in the horizontal or vertical line of symmetry. That is, the total number of legitimate configurations is four times the total number of A-restricted configurations.

There are essentially two different configurations for the pair (A, D). Either A and D are in the same row or A and D are in adjacent rows, but in the same column.

In the first case, there are six possible choices for B such that A and B are not in the same row. This leaves two choices for C, a total of 12 = 6 × 2 choices for the pair (B, C). Now there are exactly two ways for A and D to be in the same row, so this configuration provides 24 = 2 × 12 choices for the quadruple (A, B, C, D).

In the second case, there are two legitimate ways of placing B in the first column, from which there arises exactly one legitimate choice for C. Alternatively, there are three ways to place B in the second column, leading to three legitimate choices for C. The total number of choices for a (B,C) pair is thus 11 = (2 × 1) + (3 × 3). But there are three ways for A and D to be in this configuration, giving a total of 33 = 3 × 11 choices for (A, B, C, D) in this configuration.

Thus, the total number of arrangements is: 5,472 = 4 × 24 × (24 + 33).

270 On successive days the numbers of items sent to me are: 1, 1 + 2 = 3, 1 + 2 + 3 = 6, 1 + 2 + 3 + 4 = 10, ..., 1 + 2 + ... + 11 + 12 = 78.

The total is 1 + 3 + 6 + 10 + 15 + 21 + 28 + 36 + 45 + 55 + 66 + 78 = 364, which is not quite enough to last until next Christmas.

271 Day eight. It was a goose.

On day one, I received 1 present.

On day two, I received 2 + 1 = 3 presents, meaning 4 in total by the end of day two.

On day three, I received 3 + 2 + 1 = 6 presents, so 10 in total by the end of day three.

On day four, I received 10 presents, so 20 by the end of day four.

On day five, I received 15 presents, so 35 by the end of day five.

On day six, I received 21 presents, so 56 by the end of day six.

On day seven, I received 28 presents, so 84 by the end of day seven.

On day eight, I received 36 presents, so 120 by the end of day eight. So it was on day eight that I received my 100th gift.

At the start of day eight, I've had 84 presents. So I want to know the 16th present to arrive on day eight. And on day eight I received eight maids a milking, seven swans a swimming – that's 15 presents – and then six geese a laying. So the 16th present on day eight, and so the 100th present overall, was a goose.

The numbers of presents received on each day are called triangle numbers.

272 'Mulled' here is an anagram indicator and 'wine thinker blamed it' is an anagram of 'In The Bleak Midwinter', the Christmas carol based on the poem by Christina Rossetti.

273 It is possible.

274 There are 480 different ways to arrange your books with the cookery and Rudolf books not being next to one another.

To see why, we first notice that N objects can be ordered in $N \times (N - 1) \times ... \times 1$ ways because we have N choices for the first object, $N - 1$ remain for the second choice, $N - 2$ for the second, and so on.

The number of arrangements that separate the Rudolf and the cookery book is # total arrangements – #arrangements with Rudolf next to the cookery book.

The total number of arrangements of the six books is $6 \times 5 \times 4 \times 3 \times 2 \times 1 = 720$. If we glue the Rudolf and the cookery books together, then the books can be arranged in $5 \times 4 \times 3 \times 2 \times 1 = 120$ ways.

Rudolf can be glued to the left or the right of the cookery book. So the number of arrangements with the Rudolf and the cookery books next to one another is $2 \times 120 = 240$. Therefore, the total number of ways of arranging your books with the Rudolf and cookery books not being next to one another is $720 - 240 = 480$.

275 **First draw:** there are three green balls out of six in total.

Second draw: there are two green balls out of five in total.

Third draw:– there is one green ball out of four in total.

$3/6 \times 2/5 \times 1/4 = 6/120$

That is, 1 in 20 (or 5 per cent).

276 255.

277 Neither. There is exactly the same eggnog in the brandy glass as brandy in the eggnog cup. Both vessels now have the same volume of liquid as they did at the beginning so we have replaced all the eggnog that is in the brandy glass with brandy in the eggnog cup.

278 54.

279 9.

280 On the 12th day you receive $P12 = 1 + 2 + 3 + 4 + ... + 12 = 78$ presents.
On the 100th day the sum is longer. Instead, we can recognise that the
number of presents received on day N is the Nth triangular number
(imagine laying snooker balls out in a triangle when racking up – the
top row has 1 ball, the second 2, the third 3 etc. – the total number of
balls in the triangle is a triangular number). The formula for triangular
numbers comes from pairing up the different number of presents on
different days. For example, with 12 days we can pair day 12 with day 1
to give 13 presents. We can then pair day 11 with day 2 to give another
12 presents and so on. In total we have $12/2 = 6$ sets of 13 presents,
which is $6* 13 = 78$ presents. For a more general number of days, N, the
formula for the Nth triangular number is $PN = N*(N + 1)/2$. Plugging
$N=100$ into the formula gives $P100 = 100*101/2 = 50*101 = 5050$
presents on the 100th day.

281 The first person must clink 49 new glasses, the second 48 (because they have already clinked with the first person), the third 47 and so on until the last person who doesn't have any new clinks to make because everyone has already clinked with them. So the total number of clinks is given by 49 + 48 + 47 + ... This can be recognised as the 49th triangular number for which the formula is 49*50/2 = 1,225. More intuitively, we can pair the person making the 49 clinks with the person making only 1 to get a total of 50. We can then pair the 48 clinker with the 2 clinker and so on until we pair the 26 clinker with the 24 clinker, leaving only the 25 clinker and the person who doesn't make any new clinks. So we have 24 pairs of 50 clinks and one set of 25 giving 24*50 + 25 = 1,225 clinks in total. This will take 20 minutes and 25 seconds, so the first clink must occur at 11:39:36 for the last one to occur on the stroke of midnight.

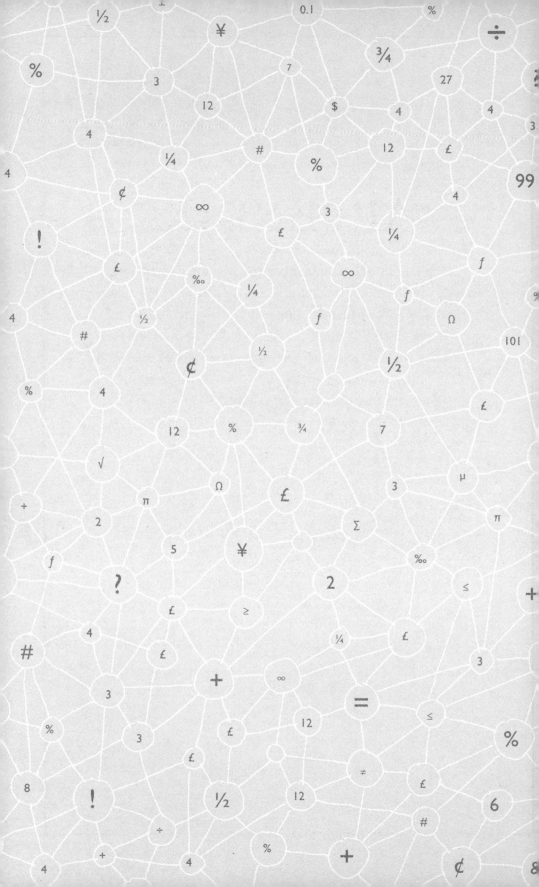

APPENDIX

Today Presenters

Jack de Manio (1958–71)

Robert Hudson (1964–68)

John Timpson
(1964, 1970–76, 1978–86)

Robert Robinson (1971–74)

Barry Norman (1974–76)

Desmond Lynam (1974–75)

Paul Barnes (1975–77)

Brian Redhead (1975–93)

Gillian Reynolds (1976)

Nigel Rees (1976–78)

Libby Purves (1978–81)

Peter Hobday (1983–96)

Jenni Murray (1985–87)

Sue MacGregor (1984–2002)

Anna Ford (1993–99)

Andrew Marr (2005–14)

Edward Stourton (1999–2009)

Carolyn Quinn (2004–08)

Evan Davis (2007–14)

James Naughtie (1994–2015)

Sarah Montague (2001–18)

John Humphrys (1987–)

Justin Webb (2009–)

Mishal Husain (2013–)

Nick Robinson (2015–)

Martha Kearney (2018–)

NEWSREADERS

Chris Aldridge

Corrie Corfield

Caroline Nicholls

Neil Sleat

Zeb Soanes

Diana Speed

Kathy Clugston

Susan Rae

Charles Carroll

EDITORS

Jenny Abramsky (1986–87)

Phil Harding (1987–93)

Roger Mosey (1993–97)

John Barton (1997–98)

Rod Liddle (1998–2002)

Kevin Marsh (2002–06)

Ceri Thomas (2006–12)

Jamie Angus (2012–17)

Sarah Sands (2017–)

UK Prime Ministers

1. Sir Robert Walpole, 1721–42
2. Spencer Compton, 1st Earl of Wilmington, 1742–3
3. Henry Pelham, 1743–54
4. Thomas Pelham-Holles, 1st Duke of Newcastle, 1754–6
5. William Cavendish, Duke of Devonshire, 1756–7
6. Thomas Pelham-Holles, 1st Duke of Newcastle, 1757–62
7. John Stuart, 3rd Earl of Bute, 1762–3
8. George Grenville, 1763–5
9. Charles Watson-Wentworth, 2nd Marquess of Rockingham, 1765–6
10. William Pitt 'The Elder', 1st Earl of Chatham, 1766–8
11. Augustus Henry Fitzroy, 3rd Duke of Grafton, 1768–70
12. Lord Frederick North, 1770–82
13. Charles Watson-Wentworth, 2nd Marquess of Rockingham, 1782
14. William Petty, 2nd Earl of Shelburne, 1782–3
15. William Cavendish-Bentinck, Duke of Portland, 1783
16. William Pitt 'The Younger' 1783–1801
17. Henry Addington, 1st Viscount Sidmouth 1801–4
18. William Pitt 'The Younger' 1804–6
19. William Wyndham Grenville, 1st Baron Grenville 1806–7
20. William Cavendish-Bentinck, Duke of Portland, 1807–9
21. Spencer Perceval, 1809–12
22. Robert Banks Jenkinson, Earl of Liverpool, 1812–27
23. George Canning, 1827
24. Frederick Robinson, Viscount Goderich, 1827–8
25. Arthur Wellesley, Duke of Wellington, 1828–30
26. Charles Grey, 2nd Earl Grey, 1830–4
27. William Lamb, 2nd Viscount Melbourne, 1834
28. Arthur Wellesley, Duke of Wellington, 1834
29. Sir Robert Peel, 2nd Baronet, 1834–5
30. William Lamb, 2nd Viscount Melbourne, 1835–41
31. Sir Robert Peel, 2nd Baronet, 1841–6
32. Lord John Russell, 1st Earl Russell, 1846–52
33. Edward Smith Stanley, 14th Earl of Derby, 1852
34. George Hamilton Gordon, Earl of Aberdeen, 1852–5
35. Henry John Temple, 3rd Viscount Palmerston, 1855–8
36. Edward Smith Stanley, 14th Earl of Derby, 1858–9

37. Henry John Temple, 3rd Viscount Palmerston, 1859–65

38. Lord John Russell, 1st Earl Russell, 1865–6

39. Edward Smith Stanley, 14th Earl of Derby, 1866–8

40. Benjamin Disraeli, the Earl of Beaconsfield, 1868

41. William Ewart Gladstone, 1868–74

42. Benjamin Disraeli, the Earl of Beaconsfield, 1874–80

43. William Ewart Gladstone, 1880–5

44. Robert Gascoyne-Cecil, 3rd Marquess of Salisbury, 1885–6

45. William Ewart Gladstone, 1886

46. Robert Gascoyne-Cecil, 3rd Marquess of Salisbury, 1886–92

47. William Ewart Gladstone, 1892–4

48. Archibald Primrose, Earl of Rosebery, 1894–5

49. Robert Gascoyne-Cecil, 3rd Marquess of Salisbury, 1895–1902

50. Arthur James Balfour, 1902–5

51. Sir Henry Campbell-Bannerman, 1905–8

52. Herbert Henry Asquith, 1908–16

53. David Lloyd George, 1916–22

54. Andrew Bonar Law, 1922–3

55. Stanley Baldwin, 1923–4

56. James Ramsay MacDonald, 1924

57. Stanley Baldwin, 1924–9

58. James Ramsay MacDonald, 1929–35

59. Stanley Baldwin, 1935–7

60. Neville Chamberlain, 1937–40

61. Winston Churchill, 1940–5

62. Clement Attlee, 1945–51

63. Sir Winston Churchill, 1951–5

64. Sir Anthony Eden, 1955–7

65. Harold Macmillan, 1957–63

66. Sir Alec Douglas-Home, 1963–4

67. Harold Wilson, 1964–70

68. Sir Edward Heath, 1970–4

69. Harold Wilson, 1974–6

70. James Callaghan, 1976–9

71. Baroness Margaret Thatcher, 1979–90

72. Sir John Major, 1990–7

73. Tony Blair, 1997–2007

74. Gordon Brown, 2007–10

75. The Rt Hon David Cameron 2010–16

76. Theresa May 2016–present (2018)

US Presidents

1.   George Washington, 1789–97
2.   John Adams, 1797–1801
3.   Thomas Jefferson, 1801–9
4.   James Madison, 1809–17
5.   James Monroe, 1817–25
6.   John Quincy Adams, 1825–9
7.   Andrew Jackson, 1829–37
8.   Martin Van Buren, 1837–41
9.   William Henry Harrison, 1841
10.   John Tyler, 1841–5
11.   James K Polk, 1845–9
12.   Zachary Taylor, 1849–50
13.   Millard Fillmore, 1850–3
14.   Franklin Pierce, 1853–7
15.   James Buchanan, 1857–61
16.   Abraham Lincoln, 1861–5
17.   Andrew Johnson, 1865–9
18.   Ulysses S Grant, 1869–77
19.   Rutherford B. Hayes, 1877–81
20.   James Garfield, 1881
21.   Chester A Arthur, 1881–5
22.   Grover Cleveland, 1885–9
23.   Benjamin Harrison, 1889–93
24.   Grover Cleveland, 1893–7
25.   William McKinley, 1897–1901
26.   Theodore Roosevelt, 1901–9
27.   William Howard Taft, 1909–13
28.   Woodrow Wilson, 1913–21
29.   Warren G Harding, 1921–3
30.   Calvin Coolidge, 1923–9
31.   Herbert Hoover, 1929–33
32.   Franklin D Roosevelt, 1933–45
33.   Harry S Truman, 1945–53
34.   Dwight D Eisenhower, 1953–61
35.   John F Kennedy, 1961–3
36.   Lyndon B Johnson, 1963–9
37.   Richard M Nixon, 1969–74
38.   Gerald R Ford, 1974–7
39.   James Carter, 1977–81
40.   Ronald Reagan, 1981–9
41.   George H W Bush, 1989–93
42.   William J Clinton, 1993–2001
43.   George W Bush, 2001–9
44.   Barack Obama, 2009–17
45.   Donald J Trump, 2017–present (2018)

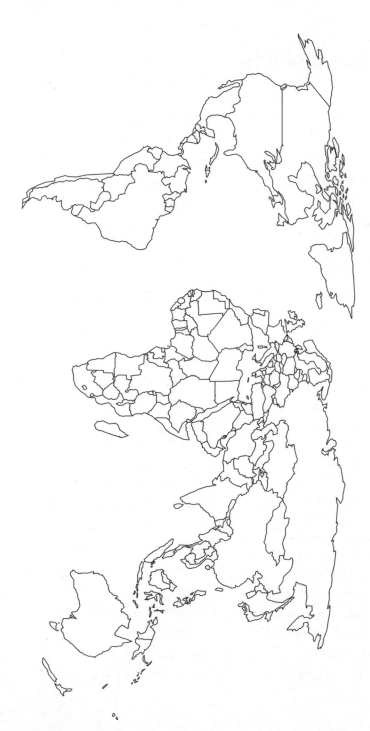

World Map

Capital Cities

Afghanistan – Kabul

Albania – Tirana

Algeria – Algiers

Andorra – Andorra La Vella

Angola – Luanda

Antigua and Barbuda – St John's

Argentina – Buenos Aires

Armenia – Yerevan

Australia – Canberra

Austria – Vienna

Azerbaijan – Baku

Bahamas, The – Nassau

Bahrain – Manama

Bangladesh – Dhaka

Barbados – Bridgetown

Belarus – Minsk

Belgium – Brussels

Belize – Belmopan

Benin – Porto-Novo

Bhutan – Thimphu

Bolivia – La Paz/Sucre

Bosnia-Herzegovina – Sarajevo

Botswana – Gaborone

Brazil – Brasília

Brunei – Bandar Seri Begawan

Bulgaria – Sofia

Burkina Faso – Ouagadougou

Burundi – Bujumbura

Cabo Verde – Praia

Cambodia – Phnom Penh

Cameroon – Yaoundé

Canada – Ottawa

Central African Republic – Bangui

Chad – Ndjamena

Chile – Santiago

China – Beijing

Colombia – Bogotá

Comoros – Moroni

Congo – Brazzaville

Congo, Democratic Republic of the
      – Kinshasa

Costa Rica – San José

Côte d'Ivoire – Yamoussoukro

Croatia – Zagreb

Cuba – Havana

Cyprus – Nicosia

Czechia – Prague

Denmark – Copenhagen

Djibouti – Djibouti

Dominica – Roseau

Dominican Republic – Santo
      Domingo

East Timor – Dili

Ecuador – Quito

Egypt – Cairo

El Salvador – San Salvador

Equatorial Guinea – Malabo

Eritrea – Asmara

Estonia – Tallinn

Ethiopia – Addis Ababa

Fiji – Suva

Finland – Helsinki

France – Paris

Gabon – Libreville

Gambia, The – Banjul

Georgia – Tbilisi

Germany – Berlin

Ghana – Accra

Greece – Athens

Grenada – St George's

Guatemala – Guatemala City

Guinea – Conakry

Guinea-Bissau – Bissau

Guyana – Georgetown

Haiti – Port-au-Prince

Honduras – Tegucigalpa

Hungary – Budapest

Iceland – Reykjavik

India – New Delhi

Indonesia – Jakarta

Iran – Tehran

Iraq – Baghdad

Ireland – Dublin

Israel – Jerusalem*

Italy – Rome

Jamaica – Kingston

Japan – Tokyo

Jordan – Amman

Kazakhstan – Astana

Kenya – Nairobi

Kiribati – Tarawa

Korea, North – Pyŏngyang

Korea, South – Seoul

Kosovo – Pristina

Kuwait – Kuwait City

Kyrgyzstan – Bishkek

Laos – Vientiane

Latvia – Riga

Lebanon – Beirut

Lesotho – Maseru

Liberia – Monrovia

Libya – Tripoli

Liechtenstein – Vaduz

Lithuania – Vilnius

Luxembourg – Luxembourg

Macedonia – Skopje

Madagascar – Antananarivo

Malawi – Lilongwe

* disputed

Malaysia – Kuala Lumpur/Putrajaya

Maldives – Malé

Mali – Bamako

Malta – Valletta

Marshall Islands – Majuro

Mauritania – Nouakchott

Mauritius – Port Louis

Mexico – Mexico City

Micronesia – Palikir

Moldova – Chisinau

Monaco – Monaco

Mongolia – Ulan Bator

Montenegro – Podgorica

Morocco – Rabat

Mozambique – Maputo

Myanmar (Burma) – Naypyidaw

Namibia – Windhoek

Nauru – Yaren

Nepal – Kathmandu

Netherlands – Amsterdam

New Zealand – Wellington

Nicaragua – Managua

Niger – Niamey

Nigeria – Abuja

Norway – Oslo

Oman – Muscat

Pakistan – Islamabad

Palau – Melekeok

Panama – Panamá

Papua New Guinea – Port Moresby

Paraguay – Asunción

Peru – Lima

Philippines – Manila

Poland – Warsaw

Portugal – Lisbon

Qatar – Doha

Romania – Bucharest

Russia – Moscow

Rwanda – Kigali

St Kitts and Nevis – Basseterre

St Lucia – Castries

St Vincent and the Grenadines – Kingstown

Samoa – Apia

San Marino – San Marino

São Tomé and Príncipe – São Tomé

Saudi Arabia – Riyadh

Senegal – Dakar

Serbia – Belgrade

Seychelles – Victoria

Sierra Leone – Freetown

Singapore – Singapore

Slovakia – Bratislava

Slovenia – Ljubljana

Solomon Islands – Honiara

Somalia – Mogadishu

South Africa – Cape Town/Pretoria/
　　Bloemfontein

Spain – Madrid

Sri Lanka – Colombo

Sudan – Khartoum

Sudan, South – Juba

Suriname – Paramaribo

Swaziland (eSwatini) – Mbabane

Sweden – Stockholm

Switzerland – Bern

Syria – Damascus

Taiwan – Taipei

Tajikistan – Dushanbe

Tanzania – Dodoma

Thailand – Bangkok

Togo – Lomé

Tonga – Nuku'alofa

Trinidad and Tobago – Port of Spain

Tunisia – Tunis

Turkey – Ankara

Turkmenistan – Ashgabat

Tuvalu – Fongafale

Uganda – Kampala

Ukraine – Kiev

United Arab Emirates – Abu Dhabi

United Kingdom – London

United States of America –
　　Washington, DC

Uruguay – Montevideo

Uzbekistan – Tashkent

Vanuatu – Port-Vila

Vatican City – Vatican City

Venezuela – Caracas

Vietnam – Hanoi

Yemen – Sana'a

Zambia – Lusaka

Zimbabwe – Harare

Periodic Table

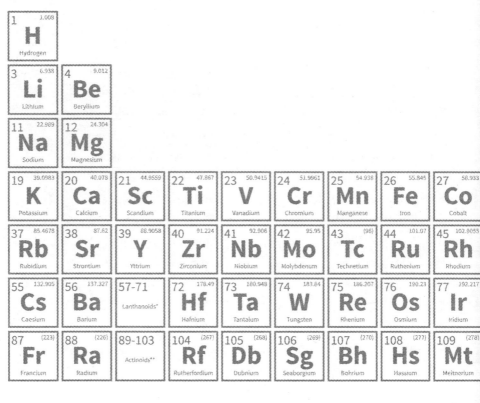

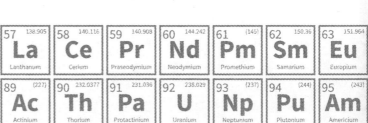

							2 4.0026 **He** Helium

5 10.806 **B** Boron	6 12.0096 **C** Carbon	7 14.0064 **N** Nitrogen	8 15.999 **O** Oxygen	9 18.998 **F** Fluorine	10 20.1797 **Ne** Neon
13 26.9815 **Al** Aluminium	14 28.084 **Si** Silicon	15 30.974 **P** Phosphorus	16 32.059 **S** Sulfur	17 35.446 **Cl** Chlorine	18 39.948 **Ar** Argon

8 58.6934 **Ni** Nickel	29 63.546 **Cu** Copper	30 65.38 **Zn** Zinc	31 69.723 **Ga** Gallium	32 72.630 **Ge** Germanium	33 74.922 **As** Arsenic	34 78.971 **Se** Selenium	35 79.901 **Br** Bromine	36 83.798 **Kr** Krypton
6 106.42 **Pd** Palladium	47 107.8682 **Ag** Silver	48 112.414 **Cd** Cadmium	49 114.818 **In** Indium	50 118.710 **Sn** Tin	51 121.760 **Sb** Antimony	52 127.60 **Te** Tellurium	53 126.904 **I** Iodine	54 131.293 **Xe** Xenon
8 195.084 **Pt** Platinum	79 196.967 **Au** Gold	80 200.592 **Hg** Mercury	81 204.382 **Tl** Thallium	82 207.2 **Pb** Lead	83 208.980 **Bi** Bismuth	84 (209) **Po** Polonium	85 (210) **At** Astatine	86 (222) **Rn** Radon
10 (281) **Ds** Darmstadtium	111 (282) **Rg** Roentgenium	112 (285) **Cn** Copernicium	113 (286) **Nh** Nihonium	114 (289) **Fl** Flerovium	115 (290) **Mc** Moscovium	116 (293) **Lv** Livermorium	117 (294) **Ts** Tennessine	118 (294) **Og** Oganesson

4 157.25 **Gd** Gadolinium	65 158.925 **Tb** Terbium	66 162.500 **Dy** Dysprosium	67 164.930 **Ho** Holmium	68 167.259 **Er** Erbium	69 168.934 **Tm** Thulium	70 173.045 **Yb** Ytterbium	71 174.9668 **Lu** Lutetium
6 (247) **Cm** Curium	97 (247) **Bk** Berkelium	98 (251) **Cf** Californium	99 (252) **Es** Einsteinium	100 (257) **Fm** Fermium	101 (258) **Md** Mendelevium	102 (259) **No** Nobelium	103 (266) **Lr** Lawrencium

Prime Numbers

A prime number is a whole number bigger than 1 that can be divided exactly by 1 and by itself but not by any other number.

2	59	137	227	313	419
3	61	139	229	317	421
5	67	149	233	331	431
7	71	151	239	337	433
11	73	157	241	347	439
13	79	163	251	349	443
17	83	167	257	353	449
19	89	173	263	359	457
23	97	179	269	367	461
29	101	181	271	373	463
31	103	191	277	379	467
37	107	193	281	383	479
41	109	197	283	389	487
43	113	199	293	397	491
47	127	211	307	401	499
53	131	223	311	409	503...

NATO Phonetic Alphabet

A – ALFA	**J** – JULIETT	**S** – SIERRA
B – BRAVO	**K** – KILO	**T** – TANGO
C – CHARLIE	**L** – LIMA	**U** – UNIFORM
D – DELTA	**M** – MIKE	**V** – VICTOR
E – ECHO	**N** – NOVEMBER	**W** – WHISKEY
F – FOXTROT	**O** – OSCAR	**X** – XRAY
G – GOLF	**P** – PAPA	**Y** – YANKEE
H – HOTEL	**Q** – QUEBEC	**Z** – ZULU
I – INDIA	**R** – ROMEO	

Further Reading

Bellos, Alex (2018) *Puzzle Ninja: Pit Your Wits Against The Japanese Puzzle Masters*, London: Guardian Faber Publishing

Carver, Hywel (2017) *Sodding Sums: The 10% of Maths You Actually Need*, London: Kyle Books

Griller, Daniel (2017) *Elastic Numbers: 108 Puzzles for the Serious Problem Solver*, Rational Falcon

Mason, Mark (2017) *Question Time: A Journey Round Britain's Quizzes*, London: Weidenfeld & Nicolson

Monkman, Bobby and Seagull, Bobby (2017) *The Monkman and Seagull Quiz Book*, London: Eyewear Publishing

Neale, Vicky (2017) *Closing the Gap: The Quest to Understand Prime Numbers*, Oxford: Oxford University Press

Seagull, Bobby (2018) *The Life-Changing Magic of Numbers*, London: Virgin Books

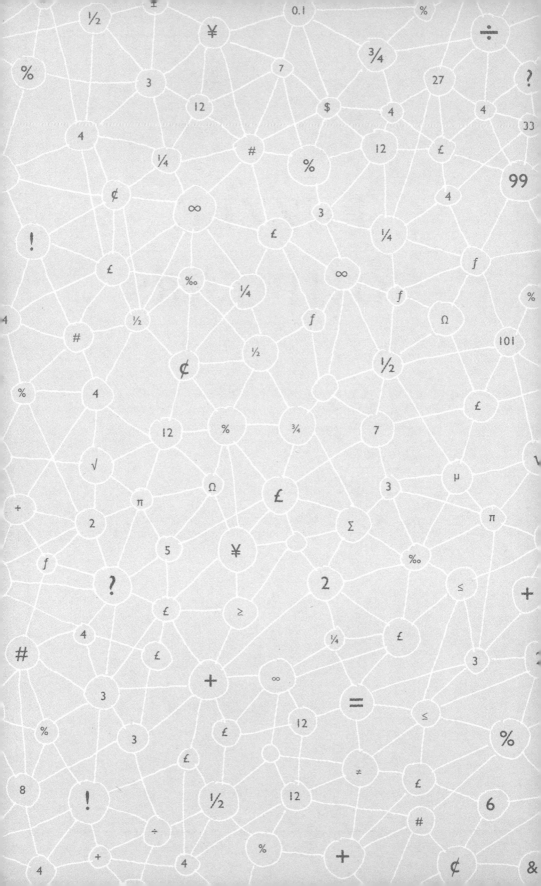

PUZZLE
COMPILERS

Alex Bellos
Puzzle blogger at the *Guardian* and author.

Professor Chris Budd OBE
Department for Mathematical Sciences at the University of Bath.

Paul Carden
Senior Lecturer in the Computer Science and Informatics Department,
London South Bank University.

Hywel Carver
Author of *Sodding Sums: The 10% of Maths You Actually Need.*

Rob Eastaway
Director of Maths Inspiration, a national programme of maths lecture
shows for teenagers, and the author of several books on maths and
thinking skills. www.robeastaway.com/blog.

Dr Nicos Georgiou
Senior Lecturer of Mathematics at the University of Sussex.

Daniel Griller
Mathematics teacher, Olympiad problem composer, and author of the
puzzle book *Elastic Numbers.*

Dr Steve Humble MBE
Head of Education, Newcastle University.

Hugh Hunt
Reader in Engineering Dynamics and Vibration at Trinity College,
Cambridge.

Naoki Inaba
Selected by Alex Bellos, author of *Puzzle Ninja: Pit Your Wits Against
the Japanese Puzzle Masters.*

Institute and Faculty of Actuaries
The IFoA is a leading international membership organisation which
educates, develops and regulates actuaries as experts in risk. This
professional body aims to put the public interest first.

Dr Gihan Marasingha
Senior lecturer in Mathematics, University of Exeter.

Chris Maslanka
Chris Maslanka is a British writer and broadcaster, specialising in puzzles and problem solving. He is also the Enigmatist of St Catherine's College, Oxford.

Mark Mason
Author of the book *Question Time: A Journey Round Britain's Quizzes*.

Mensa
The High IQ Society.

Professor Jonathan Mestel
Professor of Applied Mathematics, Imperial College London.

Tetsuya Miyamoto
Selected by Alex Bellos, author of *Puzzle Ninja: Pit Your Wits Against the Japanese Puzzle Masters*.

Dr Daniel Mortlock
Lecturer in Astro-Statistics, Imperial College London and Guest Professor, Stockholm University.

Vicky Neale
Whitehead Lecturer at the Mathematical Institute and Balliol College, University of Oxford, and the author of the new book *Closing the Gap: the quest to understand prime numbers*.

NRICH project, University of Cambridge (nrich.maths.org)
The University of Cambridge's NRICH website (nrich.maths.org) provides free mathematics resources designed to challenge, inspire and engage all ages from 3 to 18. NRICH activities focus on problem-solving and encourage rich mathematical thinking, discussion, exploration and discovery. Students are invited to submit solutions to 'live' problems on the site, with featured solutions published online. The resources

include extensive support for teachers, and are designed to build students' mathematical reasoning, perseverance, ability to apply knowledge creatively in unfamiliar contexts, and confidence in tackling new challenges.

'Perplex'
A brain-teaser app made by the UK Mathematics Trust and The Open University.

Dr Jennifer Rogers
Vice president for external affairs for The Royal Statistical Society and Director of Statistical Consultancy at the University of Oxford.

Professor Gregory Sankaran
Department for Mathematical Sciences at the University of Bath.

School of Mathematics and Statistics at the University of Sheffield
The puzzles that appear have come from undergraduates to emeritus professors via every academic rank and technical staff in between. They were born or developed at weekly coffee mornings, with further contributions and improvements suggested there from a broad range of people.

School of Mathematics at the University of Manchester

Bobby Seagull
Bobby Seagull is a Cambridge University Doctorate student researching maths anxiety/phobia and a school maths teacher. He is also an ambassador for the charity National Numeracy, a presenter for an Open University course on personal finance for young adults, and a guest *Financial Times Money* columnist. He is co-author of the *Monkman & Seagull Quiz Book* and his own book *The Life Changing Magic of Numbers*. Outside of all things numerical, he is a long-suffering West Ham fan.

Dr Roger Teichmann
Lecturer in Philosophy, St Hilda's College, University of Oxford.

Tes

Tes hosts a full curriculum of maths lessons developed in collaboration with White Rose Maths, available free on its resources site

UK Mathematics Trust (www.ukmt.org.uk)

A charity based at the University of Leeds whose aim is to advance the education of young people in mathematics, primarily through the organisation and running of national mathematics competitions. UKMT problems are written by dedicated volunteer problem setters.

Dr Lynda White

Principal Teaching Fellow in Experimental Design in the Department of Mathematics at Imperial College London.

Dr Kit Yates

Kit Yates is a Senior Lecturer in Mathematical Biology at the University of Bath and a popular science writer. His research into Mathematical Biology has been covered by the BBC, the *Guardian*, the *Telegraph*, the *Mail*, RTE and Reuters, among others. He regularly contributes his own articles about the everyday practical applications of mathematics to publications like *Scientific American* and *The Times*. He is a director and trustee of MathsWorldUK, the UK's Mathematical Museum project. Kit is currently writing his first popular science book, *The Maths of Life and Death*, which will be published in the autumn of 2019.

Nobuyuki Yoshigahara

Selected by Alex Bellos, author of *Puzzle Ninja, Pit Your Wits Against The Japanese Puzzle Masters*.

BBC RADIO 4

An Hachette UK Company
www.hachette.co.uk

First published in Great Britain in 2018 by Cassell,
an imprint of Octopus Publishing Group Ltd
Carmelite House
50 Victoria Embankment
London EC4Y 0DZ
www.octopusbooks.co.uk

Chapter introductions by Tom Feilden.

ISBN 978-1-78840-058-9

A CIP catalogue record for this book is available from the
British Library.

Printed and bound by CPI Group (UK) Ltd, Croydon, C R0 4YY

10 9 8 7 6 5 4 3 2 1

Commissioning Editor Romilly Morgan
Junior Editor Ella Parsons
Assistant Editor Ellie Corbett
Designer Jack Storey
Typesetter Jeremy Tilston
Copy Editor Lesley Malkin
Senior Production Manager Peter Hunt

Picture Credits

Dreamstime.com Andreylobachev 108; Dave
Jones 28, 142; Microvone 272; Pytyczech 267;
Zts 148. **Noun Project** Amanda Widjaya 24;
Cecilia Morales 65; Enzo Marti 37; Forget Me
Not 91; Gerardo Martín Martínez 109; Guilherme
Furtado 43; hendra sudibyo 126; jon trillana 35;
Lucas fhñe 42.